Sudden Splendor

SUDDEN SPLENDOR

THE STORY OF MABEL DIGBY

by

M. K. Richardson

SHEED & WARD: NEW YORK

B
D

Nihil Obstat
   Daniel Duivesteijn, S.T.D.
   Censor Deputatus

Imprimatur
   E. Morrogh Bernard
   Vic. Gen.

Westmonasterii, die 3a Octobris, 1955

CONTENTS

Introduction

SCHOLARLY *Lives* have a limited appeal, and the influence of a dynamic personality is sometimes restricted by too learned a treatment. Fact, more interesting than fiction, can be perhaps presented in a form familiar to the reading habits of the average person of today without losing any of its truth. In this presentation of Mabel Digby I have introduced nothing that does not have ample warrant. Besides the official *Life* in English by Ann Pollen (John Murray 1914) and the contemporary French *Life* which made use of much of the same collected material, I have had access to unpublished Journals, to short biographies of those religious who are mentioned in these pages, and to day-by-day accounts of different Houses, covering such events as the flooding of the Loire, the foundation of the Training College, and the closing of the French convents. These have often included remarks and conversations recorded verbatim, and are full of those intimate details that give vivid life to the recital, like the gray kid gloves of the liquidator and his excuse that he must see his family off to the seaside.

Privately published conferences and letters of Reverend Mother Digby and the words lovingly remembered by her spiritual daughters and friends give her habitual thoughts, and wherever I have shown her speaking or reflecting, I have made literal use of these, though not always in their original context.

I have received confirmation of my interpretation of her influence from those still living who knew her and who as children received the impression that she was a woman who combined great strength with extreme gentleness, a woman who was "royal," who attracted by her holiness, who was "magnificent" in her courage under pain. Yet characteristically the box of large chocolates she gave each child in 1887 to celebrate the Queen's Golden Jubilee is also remembered and the naval battle she organized one holiday and fought out in laundry tubs on the Roehampton lake. The septuagenarian of today recalls that, when she was a tiny child, Mother Digby placed her in her own chapel stall, then knelt in prayer. The child's impulse to scramble down and make the Reverend Mother sit instead was checked by awe at the sight of her absorption in God. And one who saw her in the last years still feels as then "the sudden desire to kneel down, as though the Blessed Sacrament were passing."

If some of her vital personality reaches the readers of this Life, perhaps the unscholarly treatment will find its justification.

I · The Restless Heart
1835-1852

Chapter One

1835

SIMON DIGBY let the heavy door close behind him. For a moment he stood at the head of the stairs, shutting out the sight of the blackcoated doctor gently breaking the brutal news, the professionally sympathetic nurse whose eyes had shown a gleam of human pity. The child dead, the mother dying. No. It could not happen to him. His wife so full of life . . . she must not die. They did not want him near her. They would not let him stay beside her. Dying. Slipping away from him, as though she had never been his. Impossibly remote from him now, with all the preoccupation of death around her.

He stumbled down the stairs. In the hall, the mask of a fox looked down on him with cynical glass eyes, sharp ears alert. His whip lay on the table where he had hastily thrown it. From the housekeeper's room, the nursemaid holding two-year-old Gertrude in her arms watched him with goggling interest, as she quietened Kenelm and Geraldine squabbling over their toys on the floor. He strode past them, snatching up his whip, closing his ears to Kenelm's cry of greeting. He must get away; he must not stay in this house waiting passively for the next message to be brought him. The child dead, the mother dying. No.

He was out into the yard and had the stable door open

before the groom could run out after him. In the box, his big hunter heard him coming and moved excitedly. The horse nuzzled him while the saddle was put on and the straps adjusted. The groom's words were checked by a glance at his master's face. Simon swung himself astride and the horse shook his head. Gathering the reins, he rode out of the yard, and as they turned into the avenue, he urged him into a canter that took them away from the house, silent now and hostile, so smiling when five years before he had brought home his wife. At the sound of his horse's hoofs, a flight of rooks rose from the elms, blacked ragged wings against the clear-washed blue of the April sky. The child dead, the mother dying.

On the high road, muddy and deep-rutted, he galloped blindly forward, until the clustering roofs and church tower of Staines came in view. Then he checked. He could not bear to see people now, people going about their ordinary business, laughing, buying, gossiping, as if there was no one whose life was ebbing, whose going was a pain that racked his body. He made for the river, swollen and swift-flowing. Tufts of matted twigs and grasses, broken limbs of trees, were swirling down, rising to the surface, catching for a moment or two in the overhanging willows whose feet were aswim in the flood waters, and then, wrenched away by the stream, were submerged in the ice-gray waves.

Life was flowing before him, he reflected bitterly, and he stood powerless to stop it. Life had brought him Elizabeth Anne Morse, his own Ella, unexpected, undeserved, he the nobody from Kildare and she the heiress of Sprowton Hall. He saw her again as when he had stood, shy, awkwardly bored, in the crowd at the ball at Kensington Palace. Her white shoulders rose from the low cut dress of blue velvet; her head was set proudly gracious like a queen's. The dark brown curls clustered round a face where melting brown eyes looked out from under delicately shaped eyebrows, looked out at him with kindliness.

The old King, George IV, had turned to watch Ella in all the freshness of her early twenties, surrounded by her band of admirers. And yet she had danced with him, and liked it though he could not make her mind sparkle as could his cousin Kenelm Digby or his literary friends. He had noticed the clear rosiness of her cheeks, the straight nose, the determined set of the mouth. A strange jealousy had filled him when he heard Charles X of France speak of her as "the White Rose of England." It was worse when they whispered that the King of the Belgians was in the running for her hand. And then she had given herself to him, who could speak to her neither in Latin nor Greek, not in French, Italian, German, or Spanish, quote no poems to her, discuss no weighty matters of international policy, but just offer her his plain heart and all its devotion.

He loved the woman in her as she loved the man in him. Her books, his horses, were of secondary importance. They did not matter when she smiled at him and showed him his firstborn son, Kenelm, lying beside her. He saw her again with Geraldine's curly head pressed against hers; and down on her knees on the floor with the two older children standing by, and her arms outstretched to little Gertrude, enticing her to walk. Memory crowded on memory, the laughter, the queenliness, the maturing motherliness, the wifely trust and pride in him.

Then the floating branch he had been watching detached itself from the eddying swirl by the bank and was sucked under by the current. A gray cloud spread across the sky and chased shadows over the sodden meadows. A gaunt line of pollarded willows stood out lonely against the river. Simon turned his horse, and made for the higher ground, riding through the flood-waters, sending the hoofs splashing reck-lessly in the pools and rushy streamlets.

On the slopes of the hills there were lambs, standing beside their mothers. He rode quickly past, not wishing to look at the season's mystery of life. The child dead, the mother dying. How long, O Lord, how long? The beechwood closed in on him, gray trunks soaked with black rainstreaks, green moss brilliant against the bark. A sudden shower swept through the branches and pattered on the russet leaves of autumn heaped beneath. His horse shied as a fox broke covert and streaked down the grassy slopes. Red squirrels leaped before him from tree to tree. This was his kingdom, the kingdom of the open country, wind, sun, and horses. Yet what was it to him now? This love had been displaced by a greater. He could not find his way back into its peace.

The April sunlight fell coldly on the flooded country below him. His horse was beginning to show signs of fatigue. Simon Digby faced at length toward home, as twilight crept over wood and meadow. He saw the lights in the cottages of Staines as he turned at the high road and went down the avenue of brooding elms that led to Ashford House. It rose before him, shuttered and still. The groom ran out at the sound of his horse's hoofs. He threw him the reins. The man was muttering something. What was it? That he was wanted within? He must brace himself for the last truth. Wearily he pushed open the door and walked into the hall.

The doctor was there, pulling on his gloves and buttoning his greatcoat. Why was the fellow smiling?

"My dear Mr. Digby, I was afraid I should miss you. Excellent news. Your wife will live. Soon after you had left the child uttered a cry. The mother heard and she has asked for the child. Yes, she will want to see you now!"

Simon ran up the stairs two at a time and gently opened the door. Ella, pale and exhausted, smiled at him with all her heart in her eyes. He knelt beside her, too full of joy for words.

"Aren't you going to look at our child?" she murmured at last. "A girl. Shall we call her Mabel?"

He turned from his wife to the little creature in the cot. She was very tiny, pink and crumpled-looking, eyes fast shut and closed hands. His daughter. Alive, not dead. He nearly laughed aloud. The sorrow and pain of the day sloughed from him. His daughter, especially his at the cost of his pain.

Chapter Two

1842

THE old man straightened his back as he stood up at the end of the row of strawberries. He wiped the sweat from under his cap, and paused, looking out beyond the kitchen garden, and down the hillside. There were silvery glimpses of the Avon between the trees, shimmering under the June heat. He looked up toward the house, with its handsome classic portico set in the midst of a central octagon, and its low wings on each side. Good and solid, a bit like the new owners. Highly respectable. Like most of the folks who went driving through the city nowadays. Mr. Digby knew how to ride; knew a horse when he saw one. Mrs. Digby had the looks.

He was too old to take much interest in the children. Master Kenelm was at school. Miss Geraldine wasn't his sort at all with her walking in the alley between the hedges with a prayer book in her hand. The baby boy Essex seemed a healthy youngster. He'd never seen the little girl, Gertrude, whose death at three was still spoken of by the nurse as the flight of a little angel to heaven.

He grinned to himself, as he caught sight of a small girl sitting on the stone balustrade of the terrace that stretched in front of the house. Not much of the angel about Miss Mabel. She was the one for him. Not a blink when her father lashed her fingers holding on to the pommel as her Exmoor pony was plunging among the great horses at the Duke of Grafton's stag hunt. She had the straightest back at the age of seven of any of the ladies he knew. Not a blink either when he set a baby owl before her that he'd fetched down from the rafters of the barn, all fluff and hooked beak and swivelling head. She'd taken the little creature and tamed it herself. Not a blink when she fell down the old well and hung on to the chain above the black water until he'd come and pulled her out. It was his heart and not hers that had stood still to watch her dangling her short fat legs over the nursery window-sill three stories up, because they'd locked her in there for naughtiness. He waved to the child across the terraces, and stooped to loosen the next layer of net from the strawberries.

Mabel Digby saw the wave. Poor old George, he must be very hot and tired. The carriage had not come from the yard yet. There would be time to go and help him. She was tired of sitting in her clean white dress by the stone vase, just watching the ants run around. She slipped down from her perch and crossed the grass, making for the shrubbery that led to the kitchen garden.

"Miss Mabel!"

Mademoiselle had seen her. Mademoiselle was bearing down on her, through the rosebeds. Mabel glanced round. There was a watering can, and a squirt upright in the water. She seized it, drew up the piston, heard the water sucked into the cylinder. Point-blank aim. Mademoiselle was uttering outraged cries as Mabel disappeared into the bushes.

"Good morning, George."

The old man turned on his knees. The demure little girl in her pretty muslin frock stood beside him.

"I've come to help you pick the strawberries."

"That's real kind of you, Miss Mabel. Aren't you doing lessons today?"

She had not wasted time. She was kneeling alongside and the red berries, fat and juicy, were going quickly into the basket.

"No. It's a holiday and I'm going with my mother into Bath."

"You're a lucky young lady to have book learning. They never gave me any edication."

Mabel sighed. "That's what my mother said. I asked her why I must be educated. She says I've a mind that needs cultivating."

"Like my plants," George commented. "Never mind, Miss Mabel. When you're grown up, you can leave your old books and just ride your horses until you're married."

Mabel sighed again. "No, George. My mother says education must go on all my life."

"Well, you'll get a fresh crop of strawberries each year. Your mother's right, I expect. You've got to go on planting and watering and weeding. Your mother's a fine lady."

Mabel nodded. "I said that to Papa. I said, 'They say Mama's a woman of mind. Have I got any mind, Papa?'"

"And what did your papa say?"

"'About as much as a pin's head.' In that case, George, I don't think I need to work so hard, do you?"

The basket was getting fuller as the child's nimble fingers worked with the old man's gnarled ones. They paused at the end of the long row.

"There's the carriage in front of the door. I'll have to be going now."

She walked back, smoothing her dress where kneeling had

creased the muslin. How lovely her mother looked, sitting back gracefully in the carriage! And how handsome her father! Geraldine, fair and neat, was in there already, and the driver had the reins gathered into his hands.

"Mabel, where have you been?"

Simon Digby sounded a little put out. He did not like waiting even for this special favorite of his.

"No need to ask. Look at her dress."

Her mother's voice was calm as impersonal justice, accuser and judge in one.

Mabel glanced down. There were red streaks that could only have been made by juice of ripe strawberries.

"Oh, Mabel," cried Geraldine, shocked at the disclosure of gluttony.

"As you don't know how to exercise self-control, you will stay at home today. Simon, we had better go straightaway."

Mabel's deep blue eyes turned toward her father. He was not looking at her. There was no hope of defense from that quarter. Her mouth shut in a tight line. The wheels began to turn, and the carriage drew out along the drive. She watched it disappear beyond the bend between the trees, then walked sadly back into the house.

In the carriage Mrs. Digby was saying to her husband, "That child will be either a devil or a saint."

"You are a wicked little thing!" Mademoiselle's shrill tones echoed through the hall, as Mabel stood before her. "When your parents return tonight, I shall tell them. Yes, indeed, everything. Your lessons not done. Your room left in disorder. And now this . . . this squirt! Why are you not like Miss Geraldine?"

Why, why? Mabel knew no answer. She stood silently revolving this puzzle. Mademoiselle's charges struck the outside only of her consciousness.

"Tonight when I have told your dear Mama all that you

have done, there will be no dessert for you. For Miss Geraldine, yes. But for Miss Mabel, no."

She was gone. The old butler opened the dining room door softly and beckoned.

"Miss Mabel," he whispered, "here's a peach. Where's your pocket?"

He slipped a handful of ratafias into it. He pushed her quietly out, before she had found her tongue.

How strange people were! So kind, so unkind. And how queer it was that kindness or unkindness just touched the edge of you when your heart was sore because the people you really loved had misunderstood you. She went miserably through the house and out across the yard to the stables. She ran her fingers through the neck feathers of her owl, who blinked inscrutably at her. In the far box, her pony stamped. She laid her arm across his neck and he nuzzled her. His trust in her made the world seem more secure.

Sunshine came back with the sunny afternoon. Essex wanted to romp in the garden. Chuckling, with his fat small hand in hers, he trotted beside her, out on to the smooth grass.

Nurse called out, "Here's your battledore and shuttlecock, Miss Mabel." She watched the two children as the white feathers flew up into the air. "That'll keep them quiet for some time while I get on with my mending."

"Play something else," Essex commanded at the end of half an hour. Mabel glanced around. In the corner of the lawn her mother's bathchair was standing. She lifted her brother into it. "I'll give you a ride. Hold the handle tight."

Four-year-old Essex would follow Mabel's adored lead anywhere. He clutched the steering gear, and laughed as the chair moved off down the path.

"Faster!" he ordered as they turned through the shrubbery. Mabel pushed with more vigor.

"Faster!" The chair had gathered momentum now and it was easy to run beside it while the child's laughter rose to a shriek of delight. She needed only to keep her fingertips on the handle behind as they cantered down the path.

"Faster!" Suddenly she realized that she could not go faster, that the chair had taken charge, that the revolving wheels were no longer hers to control. Desperately she tried to hang on. The handle slipped from her grasp and she stood alone on the path while Essex yelled with laughter and the chair rushed down the hillside. Frozen with horror, she saw it crash into the bank at the bottom and overturn.

They were running past her, nurse, gardeners, maids, all in one wild rush. She saw them right the chair, and pick up a still, unconscious form, whose little arms and legs hung down and turned queerly as they carried him past her. Mademoiselle was breathing fiercely into her ear.

"You have murdered your little brother."

The undernurse had her firmly by the arm and was dragging her leaden feet back to the house, and up the stairs in the wake of the young gardener who carried that motionless burden. At the bedroom door, she was pushed on to a chair.

"Don't you dare move, you wicked girl," the maid said.

She did not want to. Through the open door she watched them pull the blinds and shut out the bright sunshine. That was what you did when someone died. Essex, her darling Essex, chuckling and laughing, hugging her with his fat arms. Lying there dead on the bed. They were bringing in basins of water, and towels and white linen bandages. What were they doing that for? The nurses were talking in hushed tones. Mademoiselle walked by her without a word. Mabel heard her summon a groom to ride into Bath and warn her parents. She came back again, holding her skirts away from the child who sat without word or movement on the chair outside. And still that little form lay on the bed. Murdered, they said, murdered. By her. She was a murderer. Would they hang her? Did it matter? Essex was dead, murdered by her.

No. Suddenly it came to her that a murderer meant to kill. She had meant only to make Essex happy. They would not believe that, but now it did not matter what they thought or what they said. Like a mist clearing from a landscape, her dread lifted and a great calm sank down into her mind. God knew everything. He saw her joy as she listened to her brother's laughter in that minute before the chair slipped from her hands. He saw her agony now as the murmur of shocked voices came to her through the door. God knew.

Her mother ran up the stairs and entered without a word to her. Her father followed with the doctor. The minutes dragged on, while the door remained shut between her and the brother she had killed. The sunlight moved round through the windows, and slid away, and the gray of dusk crept over the stairs and the shadows deepened. Mabel waited, silent and still, with God.

Then the doctor came out, with her mother.

"Keep him absolutely quiet, Mrs. Digby, and he'll weather this all right. There are no bones broken. He's a healthy boy. He should get over the concussion."

They did not notice the little girl. She sat on a minute more, looking at God. He had known. No need to defend herself. She slid at last off the chair. Her father came out and saw her.

"Well, Mabel," he said, putting his arm around her in a loving clasp that spoke more than words. He did not reproach her, or scold her. Her mother might. Mademoiselle had yet to be faced. Beneath everything she was hugging to herself the tremendous truth that God knew. *God knew*.

Chapter Three

1844

T H E Y reined in their horses and sat quietly looking at the scene before them, not saying much where thoughts ran side by side. Glancing down at his nine-year-old daughter, Simon felt a great wave of pride. She had his vigor, his abounding energy, his love of the open country and his sympathy with horses. Unmanageable? Only as a mare who is high-spirited: *thoroughbred,* straight, fresh as this early morning, with the dew still on the downs, glinting in the sidelong rays of the rising sun.

Mabel turned her face. Her blue eyes danced under their black brows. "Look, Papa, there are some mushrooms over there. Can I get them?" He held her reins as she dismounted and ran across to the white cluster. "Can I have your handkerchief? There are dozens here. Don't they smell good!"

"We might have them for breakfast if we gallop back."

She wrinkled her nose. "I wish we could stay here all day."

"And dodge your lessons. Mademoiselle is just beginning to think you might talk French some day. That's more than your mother thinks about your Spanish. I wish you would work a bit harder, like Geraldine."

She laughed, knowing that he did not really care for her to become a bluestocking. She was in the saddle again, breathing in the air, with her brown hair blowing from her broad forehead. A cock crowed from a farm in the valley. A flock of sheep came over the hump of the hill. A lark was singing as it mounted into the blue sky. Simon touched his horse and set off at a canter, with Mabel beside him. This was bliss for a man. He had the illusion of riding endlessly, in a timeless world where his young daughter kept pace with all his thoughts and feelings in a perpetual early summer's dawn. There would be a time when some fellow not worth the tip of her little finger would come and ask him for her hand, and she would look at him with eyes that had lost their clear candor in depths of shyness. For the present he would not think of it, but enjoy the daughter who was nearest him in all her ways. He pressed his horse to a gallop, not turning to look at Mabel, but hearing the thud of her horse's hoofs as she followed close behind.

"And I didn't lose a single mushroom," she cried, as they dismounted in the yard, before the breakfast bell had pealed.

At the table Mrs. Digby was engrossed in a letter. How quickly one got used to things! Only four years since the penny post became law, and now one almost expected a letter every day. She felt her husband's gaze and looked up.

"Why so serious?"

"Things move at such a rate nowadays. They say the Czar means to cross to England by steamboat when he visits the Queen. We shall all be following the Royal example and traveling by train."

He frowned. "Prince Albert encourages these new inventions. I shall stick to the stagecoach. I cannot conceive of a world without horses." Something would go from the beauty of the countryside if the pink coats of huntsmen were not seen or the squire no longer rode around his broad acres. He rose. "I am going to take the hunters four-in-hand this morning. They need the exercise."

Mabel slipped down from the schoolroom when she heard

15

the jingle of harness. The four horses were like brown satin, she thought; her father, tall and well-built, sitting on the box with the reins gathered in his hands, was gay and debonair like the hero of a story. He waved to her and laughed as the coach moved off. It was a pity that she could not go with him.

She drifted back to the house. There were bees hard at work in the Canterbury bells, stroking their legs against the pollen.

Through the open door of the hall the sunshine outside looked bright. It would be dusty-musty in the schoolroom. She had a little bit of a headache, but she knew that would not be taken as an excuse. She had had headaches ever since her uncle had given her a pickaback ride when she was five and had run her head against the door lintel. She had tried once getting pity because of it. Mama had said, "We must know only by your greater cheerfulness that you have a headache." So that was that.

She went across to where the heavy plush curtains were drawn now over the tall windows, and picked up the tasselled fastener that had fallen from its hook. How familiar was their warm close smell! They made her think of that awful day when, overcome with her misdeeds, she had taken refuge behind them and Mama and Papa had sat down on the seat and talked about her. The creeping horror of hearing them wonder what they could do with her, and what the future could possibly hold for her! The hopelessness of her case when even her all-wise parents despaired! And then again that sense that above and beyond and yet very close, was God, and He knew and He did not throw her over. They had not understood why, hot and tearstained, she had emerged from her hiding place and without one word had taken her scolding. She buried the remembrance of that moment as she hid her face in a bowl of red roses her mother had set in the hall. She would go to the schoolroom now, then this afternoon she would play with

Essex and Baby Eva, then say some prayers with Geraldine up and down the shrubbery alley, and then tomorrow morning she would go out again with her father before breakfast.

The sunshine through the open doors was suddenly blotted out. Intent on her thoughts, she had not heard footsteps on the drive. Now the men were standing there, darkening the day. They looked at her and remained hesitant. The young farmer from down the hill stepped forward toward her. She saw the sweat in beads on his face, white under its tan. Her heart turned cold.

"Miss Mabel," he blurted out, "it's your father. Got out of hand, they did, the horses. My wagon was there. Didn't have a minute to draw out of the way. The horses are safe. The coach has lost an axle. We've got your father here on a hurdle. Will you tell your mother?"

The bearers moved forward and Mabel caught sight of her father. His fair hair was streaked with dark red, and a thin trickle of blood came from the corner of his mouth. His eyes were closed.

The house round about Mabel seemed empty. She was alone with no one to help her. The men put down the hurdle tenderly, stooping under its weight. She did not know if he was alive or dead. She only knew that her mother must not come upon him like that. She mounted the stairs, keeping back her tears. Her hand was on her mother's door. What was she to say? Somehow she must find the words. That was what her father would expect of her. She turned the handle.

"Mama, darling, there's been an accident."

The days when he lay insensible seemed endless, hours creeping slowly round from dawn to sunset, night's sleep a respite before the awakening to another day of helpless waiting. Then at last return to consciousness roused hope in the stricken household. Simon asked to see Mabel, and she stole

17

softly into the darkened room. How white he looked lying against the pillows, with white bandages about his head! His hand was groping over the sheet toward her.

"Mabel! Where are you?"

"Here, Papa. Papa, the horses are all right. Colonel didn't get a scratch."

She felt the pressure of his hand, but his eyes were looking beyond her. She smiled at him, but there was no answering smile. He spoke again.

"Come and keep me company when you can. You can tell me what's going on. You can be my eyes . . . I've gone blind, my dear."

She fought back her grief. She must not add to his. Once more she felt the pressure of his hand on hers.

June ran into July, and, with blossoming of the ramblers, Simon Digby saw again. Mabel spent long hours in his room, reading to him, talking of the things they both held dear. The new foal was piebald. Old George had a splendid crop of peas. The thunderstorm had made the Avon overflow in the water meadows. She had found a robin's nest with a late brood.

Simon told her of her Digby ancestors—of Sir Simon Digby who did so much on Bosworth Field for Henry Tudor, of Sir Kenelm Digby who won for himself the title of Ornament of England for his great learning, and, lest pride of ancestry should be tarnished by unworthy behavior in such as her, he told her of the young Everard Digby who listened to the blandishment of priests, became a traitor to his king, tried to blow up the Parliament, was hung, drawn and quartered outside St. Paul's even as forty years later her mother's ancestor, that tricky Jesuit Henry Morse, met his death at Tyburn. Together they pondered on the family mottoes. *Deo non fortuna. Deo non armis fido.*

"I shall take *Noblesse oblige,*" Mabel declared. He laughed at her earnestness.

"Be always straight, Mabel," he counseled. "Never tell a lie. I can't bear underhand ways. You can never trust a Papist. There is always trouble where Rome is."

"But Uncle Kenelm?" Mabel queried. "We're great friends with him." Her father laughed.

"But, you see, he was brought up a Protestant, and he's passed on that good training to your cousins. Are you looking forward to staying with them again in the autumn?"

She nodded. "Yes, it's nice in Kensington. And you can have good rides in Hyde Park."

One day he summoned her to his room mysteriously. "The doctor says I may go downstairs and take a short walk. Don't let any of them know. Just you and I when no one is about." Like conspirators they crept out on to the landing and down the stairs. In the hall they looked at each other.

"We can get out by the back way," said Mabel. She knew where he would go. Leaning heavily on her shoulder, Simon Digby crossed the yard to the stables. Mabel unlatched the door.

"Colonel!"

At the sound of his master's voice, the brown hunter whinnied wildly, stamping his feet and rearing against the box. Simon steadied himself against his daughter and gently rubbed Colonel's nose, until he had quietened him. Glancing up, Mabel saw two tears rolling down her father's face.

"Time we went back," he said at last.

They struggled upstairs again. Simon sat exhausted in his chair. "If we go to Uncle Kenelm's in the autumn," said Mabel, "we shall miss the first meets."

Her father was silent a moment.

"I shall never hunt again," he said and sat looking before him. Never again. Never again feel the forward leap of a horse to the tally ho! and the streak of the hounds over the green fields. Never again take the lead in a rush across the springy heath, never again exult in the upward lift as the horse rose to the jump, or splashed through the stream, or crested the hill in the keen clean teeth of the wind. Never again. All the bright wild leaves of autumn, fiery and fierce, fallen from the trees, stirred up by the clattering hoofs, never again to be tossed up by his mount. Never again.

Mabel threw herself down on her kness before him, caught at his hand and held it tight. Only she knew the magnitude of that "never again."

Chapter Four

1851

THE MARQUIS DE CASTELBAJAC sat sunning himself in the garden of his villa at Pau, reflecting gently as the day demanded. Through the open window came bursts of laughter, young and fresh and full of the present delight. It was pleasant to think that increasing years gave the power to set young people in light-hearted surroundings, before the cares of the world engulfed them. He felt like a steward, managing his estates just for them, keeping the gracious things of life in existence so that, when the storms like those of three years ago threatened again to plunge France into revolution, they could be weathered with no loss to traditional values. Other people besides these girls would profit by their preservation.

He liked to have them about him, liked to see them looking lovely, liked to see them sitting down to cream pastries and laughing over the parting gifts of yard-long *sucre de berlingot*. Life would sober them soon enough. Such a varied bevy of them! His own Sidonie, just out of the leading strings of the nuns of the Sacred Heart, ardent and happy; Louise de Peignerolles, talking still of what she would do in her last year at school, anxious to talk grown-up philosophy with him, and to convert the world by her simple faith; the two Spaniards, Eugénie de Montijo in particular, graceful and charming in her maturing womanhood—well for men that Mother Barat had watched over her education in Paris—what damage such women could do without strong principles.

Then the Digby girls, Geraldine fair-haired, aquiline-nosed, shy as any English miss despite her twenty years, Eva the curly-haired eight-year-old, engaging in her mischief, and Mabel, too short for her sixteen years, with those deep blue fearless eyes under their black brows—his favorite, and worth both her brothers, for daring. The way she had sat the horse that had not been fully broken in! He had spent a bad two hours until she came back laughing on a docile mount he scarcely recognized. Like her father in character, not her queenly mother for whose health the family had been staying in Paris, Touraine, and now in Pau.

An interesting family, the Digbys, the intellectual mother, the genial, gay father. He liked Mr. Digby. It always amused him to watch how well he got on with the learned priests who came to the villa, while he could be quite eloquent about the relation between popery and poverty. There had been his horror when they had gone to the quiet old town of Lourdes and he had seen the squalor of some of the streets around the Château Fort, and learned that the damp old prison was actually offered by the authorities as a shelter for two families, and his equal horror at the sight of a plaster statue of the Virgin in an old Norman church in the hills. Yet his wife was reading Bossuet. There was no accounting for Englishmen.

There was the sound of chattering and suppressed mirth.

21

Along the terrace came the girls. They had finished at last the dresses he had set them to make with the bale of muslin he had bought from the pedlar this morning. Now they lined up for his opinion.

"Judgment of Paris, ladies," he laughed, turning from one young fresh form to the next. Nimble fingers, versatile imagination, frills and furbelows. Ah, but the person within, how separate dress from wearer? They pirouetted at his command. Eugénie de Montijo bore herself like an empress. He could well believe the rumors that Louis Bonaparte, forgetting his forty-four years and his ambitions, was seeking her hand. Then there was Geraldine, covered with blushes, an English rose, Louise de Peignerolles, a fiery tiger lily. He passed them all in review.

"If I must make an award where all are lovely, I give the prize to Miss Mabel Digby," he said at last. "Her dress is simple, but it suits her to perfection. May I present this box of chocolates? And, ladies, you will console yourselves by going down to the pastrycook's. He is expecting your arrival."

They moved off with merry applause.

That evening Eva was quiet and fretful. Mrs. Digby, fearing a touch of sun, sent her to bed, where she tossed restlessly. The next morning she was not well enough to go riding. Geraldine volunteered to stay, to help her mother. Mabel set off alone with Mr. Digby.

They took the road beside the swift-running Gave, shaded with trees through which they glimpsed the fields and woods and hills. From time to time they stopped to admire a quaint old church with its clustering village, picturesque when seen at a distance.

"Close up," remarked Simon Digby, "the picturesque is seen to be the haphazard and untidy."

"Father Drujon," Mabel began, but her father's face clouded

over. "I would rather you had nothing to do with that priest," he said. "He is a Jesuit."

"A Jesuit!" Mabel exclaimed with surprise. "He doesn't look like one."

"He wouldn't, but that is how they get in the thin edge of the wedge." The thin edge of the wedge. Other phrases came into his mind, as though the excitement occasioned by the Pope's restoration of the Hierarchy in England on October 7th had etched them indelibly on his memory. The angry tone of *The Times* had been an echo of his own indignation. "Pio Nono apes the pretensions of a Hildebrand. He and his clergy despatch a Cardinal Archbishop to Westminster to catch fools with his title and enslave kindred bigots by his assumption of authority and state." "Insolent . . . insidious . . . subtle and skilful . . . emissaries of darkness. . . ." The bishops of the Established Church had summed it up well in their Durham letter. "A revolting and frightful assumption, an unparalleled aggression, an attempt to subject our people to a spiritual tyranny from which they were freed at the Reformation." Aloud Simon said, "No, my dear, keep yourself from superstition. Have nothing to do with Jesuits. With all their wealth, they are always after rich heiresses."

Mabel was silent. She could not imagine herself ever falling into the state of mental sloth and ignorance in which the faith of Irish maidservants flourished. England, thank God, was free now of all that.

When they returned, they found Eva worse. Fever burned her, and she cried in delirium. Simon fetched the doctor. There had been cholera in the neighborhood the previous year.

The doctor shook his head. "I can't tell what is wrong with her," he thought, recommending a remedy to the best of his ability. But two days later, his patient was weaker. Mrs. Digby looked at the tired curly head, listless on the pillow, and saw Eva escaping from her as Gertrude had ten years

23

before. Louise de Peignerolles came, and knelt beside the bed. Eva, babbling incoherently, stared at her with unseeing eyes. Louise took a ribbon from her neck and passed it around Eva's neck.

"What are you doing?" asked Mrs. Digby.

"It's a medal of Our Lady," said the impulsive Louise. "Pray that she will cure Eva."

Mrs. Digby drew back coldly.

Madame de Castelbajac came. She shook her head when she saw the child. Then her eye lit on the medal, and she looked enquiringly at Mrs. Digby.

Eva tossed and moaned. Mrs. Digby turned to her friend in anguish. "Pray for my child," she said broken-heartedly.

The Frenchwoman looked at her, logical even in the midst of her friendship. "You are asking my prayers and yet you do not want those of Our Lady, who is all-powerful before God?"

The words cut down into Mrs. Digby's consciousness. She left the medal around Eva's neck, though she herself did not pray. Two days later the fever had gone. Pale and weak, Eva was sitting up in bed asking for her favorite dishes. But she would not let anyone take her medal from her.

The happy parties were resumed as the summer wore on. The Marquis arranged picnic excursions for them, putting his own stables at their disposition. There was always fun and laughter where the English girls were. Yet he noticed how often Mabel liked to ride ahead by herself.

She had outstripped them one afternoon, riding up a track that doubled back upon itself as it mounted, giving glimpses of an old white watermill down by the dusty highroad. At each bend it took on more and more the air of a toy, with a strip of glinting water like a bit of ribbon beside it. The track ran at last into a forest, where the hot sun scented the air with resin and the pine needles were soft underfoot.

Beyond the forest she came out on to the mountainside, where stunted bushes diapered the ground and noisy shallow streamlets careered waveringly toward the valley. She dismounted where one stream had broadened out into a pool, and let her horse drink, scooping up some of the ice-cold water for herself, too; then on to where the trees grew tall again, and outcrops of rock towered above her, and at last barred the way. Blue sky above, with white masses of cumulus cloud drifting over the great rampart of rock above her, made her feel alone, joyfully alone.

Mabel was glad that she had come upon this loveliness first by herself. The laughter and fun of the others would break something that she had found. In the quietness of the afternoon she could not hear their approach. She waited, expecting any minute to hear sounds of merriment. Silence threw back the least sound: a stone dislodged from the rock above, a trickle of water somewhere down the slope, a stir of wind in the trees. She sat her horse quietly while the minutes passed and the stillness grew around her. Then it came to her that she was not being followed, that the party had taken a different route, that she was in truth alone on the mountain side. She must retrace her way. She took one last look at the high cliff above her. The drifting clouds beyond, blue-gray with the sunlight bathing them, piled up again, and Mabel turned her horse downhill.

The sun was coming slantwise through the trees now, shafts of gold striking the red trunks and gilding the mosquitoes in their dizzy dance. When she emerged where the stunted bushes grew, the sun had gone behind a mountain and the scene looked flat and bewildering. Where was the track she had taken? Every path looked the same, with its fringe of ragged shrub, and its noisy stream. She would find the place where she had drunk and get her bearings. Surely this was it, with its clear pool under the overhanging shelf of rock. The horse splashed through to the other side, and she urged him forward. The shadows were creeping up from below, and time was getting short.

Suddenly her horse started, each muscle quivering. The path led to a sheer drop, a knife-edge over which, in foaming thundering speed, a stream was breaking in a waterfall. This was not her way. She had well and truly lost the right path. The sinking, hollow feeling inside meant she was up against real danger. This was exciting. What should she do next? She seemed to hear her mother's voice, with a piece of long-ago advice: "You did not think before that question. Go out of the room, wait a little, then come in and ask again." She laughed aloud. She was right outside the room now! Then her father's advice came into her mind: "Make one with your horse." That was it. She might be a stranger on these hills, but her horse was born and bred here.

She let the reins hang loose, and waited for his lead. Up went his head, turning to right and left, sniffing the air. Somewhere, she thought with a smile, his supper of good oats lay, and, like her, he was hungry and wanted to get to it. He shook his head, then slowly began picking his way down through the shrubs and over the streamlets, into the black shadows of the pine wood. She hoped the stories of bear-hunting that the old man at the villa had told her, waving his beret and demonstrating the best way of approach, had been tales of a distant past. Presumably the horse would scent any such danger, and anyhow, what could she do? There was no use half-trusting someone in whom you had to trust. Let him get on with it.

Eerily the trees closed around them, the air holding the warmth and incense of the afternoon. She felt one with her horse as he warily trod the ground, pausing every now and then to sniff the air, hesitant until he got his unseen bearings. Then when they seemed to have traveled hours through the gloom, the trees thinned out, she caught snatches of clear

26

sky, the horse quickened his pace, and they were out on the white dusty road, where a sudden coolness spoke of the mill-stream, and a gaggle of geese, disturbed by their passing, hissed in protest. Mabel gathered up the reins and patted his neck. "Good boy," she said, and cantered toward the villa.

They were all there to receive her, and more besides. The Marquis was marshalling his menservants with lanterns and all the horses had been mobilized. They gazed at the laughing Mabel in surprise.

"Thank God!" said the Marquis. Eugénie kissed her on both cheeks. Sidonie de Castelbajac hugged her.

"I don't know what I should have done if we'd found you dead!"

"Oh, you would have got on all right," said the embarrassed Mabel, as the appetizing smell of frying omelet reached her. "I'm very hungry." The Marquis laughed.

"Miss Mabel, you are a little late. You will have to learn our Béarnaise proverb: 'If you want to go far, you must go fast and not stop at obstacles.'"

Chapter Five

1825

T H E Digby family had moved in the autumn to Montpellier. They were in the midst of the same pleasant people who had welcomed them at Pau. There were still the same happy gatherings, parties, dinners, dances. Only, Mrs. Digby did not join her husband and her children. She stayed at home, and found her interest in books. She seemed to Geraldine and to Mabel to have withdrawn from them, to avoid being alone with them at those times when they had been accustomed to exchange ideas and talk over their impressions of the day. They noticed at mealtimes there were silences between their father and mother, that the conversation turned to trivialities or was left to them. Some of their father's geniality seemed to have grown tired.

Essex caught Mabel one day. "Papa's in a terrible rage," he said. "I heard him positively shouting at Mama just now. Do see what the matter is."

She ran down to the sitting room. Geraldine was outside the door.

"Don't go in, Mabel," she said. "Yes, I'll tell you now what it's all about. Mama wants to become a Roman Catholic."

The stark awfulness of the statement hit Mabel like a blow on the face. "Oh, no. Impossible. She couldn't. . . ."

Geraldine said again, "It's true. She told me some days ago. I thought it unbelievable, but she does mean it . . . and why shouldn't she? She has a right to think what she likes. After all, we can all interpret the Bible as we please."

"But Rome—it's the Scarlet Woman and all that. You know you can't trust a Catholic to tell the truth . . . it's all so ignorant."

The handle of the door behind them turned violently.

"If you persist in this folly, I have nothing more to say," their father cried as he flung open the door and strode out. Mabel caught up with him. Geraldine hesitated a moment, and then went into the room where her mother, very white, sat upright in the chair. She gently put her oldest daughter from her.

"Don't get mixed up in this, my dear," she said. Bossuet's words rose in her mind. "When Jesus comes in, anywhere,

He comes in with His cross." Yes, but this cross she must bear alone.

Simon Digby and Mabel walked quickly along in silence. He knew she knew the terrible truth that had been undermining their happiness. There was no need for words between them. Together they were gazing at a nightmare situation with no possibility of an awakening.

Simon was no reader. He knew the old arguments, but his wife could counter them all from her books. She knew the answers, but when she had given them in an attempt to convince him, they seemed to have lost their savor for her. He told her she would lose all her friends, that these French-women cared only for proselytizing, and not for the woman she was, that she had read too much and books had turned her mind. When she met his reproaches with silence, his voice rose in anger. Bickering and quarreling became the most ordinary thing at meals when they met, sullen silences like brooding thunder clouds when they were apart. One day he threw a letter across to her.

"It is from your mother," he said. "See what she says. If you turn Catholic, she will cast you off as her daughter, and never set eyes on you again."

Mabel looked at her mother. Mrs. Digby's face grew white, her eyes closed, there was a quiver about her lips. The wound had cut deep, even though she made no sound. Mabel looked at her father. That gay face was distorted with a hard intensity, but she understood how much pain it masked. She got up abruptly and left them, making for her bedroom. Locking the door, she sat by the window looking out on the town with its church spires and bells and comfortable houses and shops where men and women were busy with their wares and streets where carriages moved in leisurely fashion to and fro.

How she had loved it when they came here first! And now it was the same and she did not care two straws for it. It was as though all the sunshine had been drained from a landscape. All the interest in life had gone under the shadow of this thing that her mother contemplated, wrecking their joy, their very family life, covering them with unspeakable shame and disgrace. Somehow it must be stopped. She must stop it. God must stop it. She could have no allies. Geraldine was taking her mother's part, she felt, tacitly, if not yet openly. Eva, at nine, was too frightened. She was sent from the room when the arguments began. The boys did not fully understand. Religion was a thing for women. No. It rested with her, and her alone.

Mabel knelt down and prayed earnestly, over and over again, as if she would be heard for her much saying. The same plea rising from her heart, reiterated, hammering on God's heart, surely that would prevent so wicked a thing from coming to pass. She would go on kneeling, kneeling on the bare wooden floor, kneeling till her back ached, kneeling without movement even though the flies settled on her face and hands, kneeling until God heard and granted her request. Ah, but what of the insult offered to His truth? Would He not be angered by her mother's action? Wrongdoers met the wrath of God and were punished. No. He must not punish her mother. She, Mabel, would take the merited punishment, self-inflicted. She cast around in her mind what she could do. Perhaps if she slept without her pillow, if she ate no cakes and took no sugar, if she prayed into the night by the open window in the cold, she would wrest her mother's salvation from God. Then her father would be happy again.

But her prayer and penance made no impression on her mother. Mabel, frigidly polite, did not speak to her of the grief that was always with her through the summer of 1852. She knew that her mother was making visits to Monsignor Thibaud, the Bishop. She tried to comfort her father by being his secretary and constant companion. She hardly ever spoke to

Geraldine, who now took to accompanying their mother. She was working at Simon's desk one afternoon in September when Eva, white and scared, opened the door.

"Mabel, Papa says we are to come down all of us to the dining-room."

The door was open when they reached it. At one end, with his back to the window, stood Simon Digby. At the other was their mother. Between them stood Geraldine, Kenelm and Essex.

"Come in," said Simon, motioning them to stand with their brothers and sister. "Now, you will please tell your children what you have just made known to me . . . your perfidy, your shame."

Mrs. Digby lifted her head. The color seemed all drained from it, but her dignity shone out in her steady eyes.

"We have been received into the Catholic Church, Geraldine and I, by God's grace. I must follow my conscience."

"You hear," he said harshly. "That is what your mother has done to lose her soul and wreck your lives. You see that she will not relent, neither to my entreaties nor to your tears. I cannot have her contaminating my children. I am returning to England. You must each make your choice. Will you stay with your mother or will you come with me? Choose."

The silence in the room was unbearable. A clock ticked unconcernedly while Simon's words swayed to and fro in their minds. Mrs. Digby remained motionless, no gesture betraying her desires. With a little cry, the tears bathing her face, Geraldine moved over to her side, and buried her head against her shoulder. Mrs. Digby's arm went around her. Mabel looked at her, searching for a sign that was not given. Turning, she walked straight to her father.

"I promise you," she said fiercely, "whatever may happen, to remain always a faithful Protestant."

In silence Kenelm and Essex crossed to their father. Only

31

Eva was left now. Despairingly she turned from left to right, now looking at her mother, now at her father. Proudly they each left her her freedom of choice. With a little gesture of outstretched hands to her father, she faced round toward her mother.

"I shall stay with Mama always," she whispered.

The next day Simon Digby completed his arrangements for traveling back to England. He knew of a good Protestant establishment where the two boys could finish their education. Mabel should stay with him and be his companion in this undeserved loneliness which had fallen upon him.

There were no friends to see them off. Mabel, looking out of the carriage window as the miles lessened between Montpellier and England, was not sure if she ever wished to see any acquaintances again. The disgrace of her mother. . . .

Chapter Six

1852

LOUISE DE PEIGNEROLLES exulted when she learned from Monsignor of Montpellier that Mrs. Digby and Geraldine had become Catholics. She rushed off to tell the news to Eugénie de Montijo. Sidonie was there too, looking glum.

"But the Bishop has not told you everything. Mr. Digby has returned to England with the boys and Mabel. He's furious—and so is Mabel."

"Well, we must convert her," said Louise. "We must be like the importunate widow. I shall stand outside Our Lord's door and knock and knock."

Sidonie shook her head. "Mabel's got a will of iron."

"Iron can melt in fire," retorted Louise, remembering the picture of the Sacred Heart in the school chapel. "We must pray and get prayers from all sorts of people. We can't let Mabel stay outside the Church."

Sidonie was still unconvinced. She would get prayers, but perhaps God did not want Mabel to become a Catholic. There was the mystery of faith, granted to one and withheld from another. There was the mystery of God's biding His time. Louise was trying to force His hand. She herself was not sure. Perhaps He had other plans. In her perplexity she sought out Tante Clémentine in the kitchen. She was Sidonie's sure refuge when prayers were needed.

The old woman was seated with her blue apron tied around her and blue striped petticoat showing beneath. She was peeling carrots, dipping into the basket on her left, scraping, slicing, and emptying the finished lapful into the basin on her right. She looked ageless, Sidonie thought, forever peeling vegetables for the family meals, skilled fingers always at their service, mind always conversing in familiar friendship with her Lord. She turned the candid blue eyes of a child to Sidonie as she unfolded her problem.

"But, Mademoiselle Sidonie, of course, you must pray for your friend."

"She would make such a splendid Catholic," Sidonie said. "Such a rich nature . . . merry, strong, deep, fearless. It's such a shame that Mrs. Digby and Geraldine should be separated from her, or she from them. But then, if she was converted, that would leave Mr. Digby all by himself, and he is so pleasant and amiable that I couldn't bear to think of his being lonely. Of course he might be converted too, but I don't somehow think so. He's like Mabel, or she's like him. They don't talk much to each other but they seem to understand each other without words. And he just hates the Catholic Church and so does she. I don't know what to think."

"Well, Mademoiselle Sidonie, can't you pray and leave the rest to God?"

"But I'd like to be sure of what I am praying for. I wish there was someone really holy I could ask."

A lapful of sliced carrots went into the basin, then Tante Clémentine answered. "Why don't you go to see the Curé of Ars?"

Like a flash, Sidonie knew that was what she must do. "And you will come with me, Tante Clémentine," she said.

Madame de Castelbajac demurred. The journey was long, the conditions in the little town impossible. Pilgrims had now to wait for days before they could see M. Vianney. The Marquis overrode her objections.

"God save us," he said. "A pilgrimage is meant to be penitential. It's not a feast-day holiday they are embarking on. I hope Sidonie does have an uncomfortable time."

Tante Clémentine put on her best dress for the occasion, her black skirt, embroidered apron and white bonnet. She sat bolt upright as the train left Montpellier, and the beads of her rosary passed ceaselessly between her fingers. Nîmes with its Roman memories, Avignon with its towering palace of the Popes, the swift turbulent Rhône flowing along by them, these meant nothing to her. Nearly three score years and ten she had done without unfamiliar sights. Now she carried with her the home where Mary showed her Her Son, and that was enough.

They changed trains at Lyons. At the Perrache station they had to take their place in a long file before the special booking office for Ars. Sidonie put down her money.

"You'll want an eight-day ticket," the booking clerk informed her.

"But I'm returning tomorrow."

"Take my word, Mademoiselle, you'll be lucky if you return the day after tomorrow."

The train was crowded. While Tante Clémentine said her rosary, Sidonie took stock of their fellow travelers. A family of peasants, father, mother, two rosy-faced children and a little sickly baby, a shopkeeper from Marseilles, a professional man, hiding his face behind his newspaper, a couple of nuns and a schoolmaster. It was all the world *en route* for this unhistoric, unpicturesque hamlet where a saint was living. At Villefranche they got down. The two omnibuses waiting filled up before Sidonie and Tante Clémentine could reach them. On the far side of the square an ancient carriage stood. She compounded with the driver, and they climbed in. There was the hot smell of old leather where the upholstery had burst, disclosing the dirty stuffing. The horse twitched his ears beneath his straw hat, the wheels jolted over the rough road. It was very unromantic but they were on their way to Ars, one with the stream of carts and farm wagons and foot-sore trampers who were following holiness as steel a magnet.

After some miles, the driver pulled up. "There's the village," he said, pointing to a small group of houses around a square-built little church, set in the undulating countryside with its green copses and little river. The men and women along the road were walking bareheaded. Sidonie leaned forward and paid the driver his fare.

"We'll walk from here," she said. That was the way to enter Ars, as its Curé had done years before.

The square in Ars was dense with people. The crowds stretched into the church and up to the confessional. Sidonie and Tante Clémentine took their places and waited. The hot September sun scorched down, but no one minded. Little by little they moved forward until at length they were in the church porch, but by that time the sun was mellow in the west.

35

"We'll keep your place for you if you want to get a meal," a man volunteered. "You'll not get in tonight. Fix yourself up if you can at one of the inns. I'm sleeping in the fields. He shuts the church from nine to midnight, but you won't lose your place. Everyone acts fair. But better come back after twelve."

They took him at his word. There was no room for them at the inns, but they fed, sat down for a while, and then when the moon was riding high in the sky, returned to their vigil. Suddenly there was a stir in the waiting throng.

"He's coming! There he is!"

A lantern with cracked glass was moving uncertainly between church and presbytery. The Curé approached the door, bending to unlock it once more, then he held up his light to show the way. Sidonie saw a thin, stooping figure, shabby cassock covered with surplice and purple stole, white hair, and a face, lined and emaciated, in which the love of God had ennobled every feature. One glimpse of that kindness, then she heard his great peasant's boots clumping up the aisle, the pious women who helped him were moving around lighting candles, the angelus rang out, and the feet of pilgrims began another day of wearing down the stone flags and cutting their deeper traces in the heart of the confessor.

Sidonie was getting nearer when the red of dawn began to lighten the church. At six, they lit the candles on the altar, and the Curé came out from his confessional to say Mass. From her place, Sidonie saw his face lit up with joy. At the elevation tears and smiles broke over it like sunshine on deep seas. She had seen the Lyons rite before, but never as when M. Vianney celebrated. When he stretched out his arms after the elevation and lifted his eyes, standing motionless for several minutes, it seemed as if he saw his Lord, and the light of His countenance shone on that of His humble priest. Surely he was co-crucified, bearing in his measure the sins of the world. Surely he would be able to tell her how much sin blocked Mabel's way to the fullness of love.

By eight he was in the confessional again. The atmosphere in the church was stifling, heavy with the smell of humanity. The sun came through the plain windows, full on the backs of kneeling pilgrims. Tante Clémentine mopped her face with a large handkerchief. There was the scent of garlic in the air. Someone was kneeling with her warm body up against Sidonie. The first trains from Lyons were bringing the day's influx. Sidonie saw with relief that her turn was coming. She would be able to get out into the fresh air soon. She went over what she meant to say to the Curé. She must make it all clear.

Her confession over, kneeling beside that bent white head, hearing the soft words of absolution, she found it easy to tell him about Mabel Digby. There was silence the other side of the grille. Then M. Vianney spoke, "I will pray for your friend," he said. "God will soon have complete mastery over her heart."

That was all. Sidonie was outside the confessional, kneeling by the altar rails saying her penance. The statue of St. Philomena was looking down on her, with a smile, as it seemed to her fancy. She herself was smiling. Yet what had she got from her long journey and her tiresome wait? Only the promise of a saint's prayers; only the assurance of a saint that her friend would soon be conquered by her Lord.

Tante Clémentine joined her, and they left the church. The old woman was ecstatic.

"Mademoiselle Sidonie, do you know what he said to me? He said, 'Oh, love—love the good God very much!' "

That, too, was all, but back in Montpellier it was enough to light up every little household task and gild celestially every bushel of carrots.

Chapter Seven

1852

THE London parks were still bright with flowers when Simon Digby and Mabel returned. But there was a nip in the early air as they took their ride down Rotten Row and spiders' webs, dew-pearled, tied the golden sunflowers to the purple Michaelmas daisies. Russet leaves drifted across the Serpentine and gardeners with their besoms swept the brown piles together and the blue smoke curled up.

Mabel was happiest helping her father with his letters and accounts, a better hand at business than he was himself, and going for rides and drives with him. He was pleased to take her in the new light victoria out from the city, riverwards through Kew to Twickenham and Richmond, where the lawns ran down green to the smooth-flowing water, and the warm red-brick walls shut in house and pleasance and orchard and kitchen garden. The comfortable mulberry trees seemed to him to be thoroughly English and thoroughly Protestant. The great calm trees of Richmond Park, under which the deer cropped green grass, had none of the disquieting beauty of pine forest and mountain goat, and the bells of country churches heard over the meadows on a Sunday evening when the shadows lengthened from the elm borders were very different from the unmelodious sacring bells ringing out at daybreak in the Béarnaise belfries.

October sunshine disappeared with the golden leaves. Rain soddened the ground. Damp fogs, yellowed by London smoke, drifted up the river.

"What is the matter with you?" Simon asked Mabel one late November day. "You have been over an hour with that letter. Aren't you well?"

Mabel pulled herself together.

"Only tired, Papa. I don't seem to have any energy. I shall probably be all right tomorrow."

But the next day found her still listless. Her headache was always there. She had no appetite and the gray view from the window depressed her. When a little cough began and refused to yield to syrops and possets, Simon grew really alarmed and called in the doctor. He gave her a thorough overhaul, then took Mr. Digby aside.

"You'll have to take great care if her health is not to be permanently ruined. If she stays the winter here in England, she will almost certainly go into a decline. What she needs is the soft air of the Midi. I should advise sending her to join her mother."

He looked shrewdly at Simon Digby, knowing what gossip was saying.

"The last thing I want," Simon answered. "The last thing she wants, too."

The doctor nodded. "And therein lies your safety. You will excuse my speaking out plainly. These last years I have met your problem in a professional way many a time. It's part of the general unrest of women. Give them something different to think about and their religious troubles get forgotten. At the moment I am to put Miss Florence Nightingale in touch with some hospital that will help to train her. Four years ago she was in Rome. She picked up a beautiful little girl of five from the gutter and could think of no better course than to entrust her to the Sacred Heart nuns at the Trinità dei Monti.

She made a retreat there finally, though she had gone first shaking in her shoes. There was a nun who wisely told her that it's useless to separate oneself from people to try and do the will of God. She wants to help others. She tells me that there is no training in the Church of England compared to that of the Catholic nun. There is nothing like the training which the Sacred Heart or the Order of St. Vincent gives to women. She has approached Father Manning. . . ."

"The pervert Archdeacon," Simon interrupted. "So he's back in England again?"

"He preached this June in Horseferry Road chapel," said the doctor. "Give him his due. He will not receive Miss Nightingale into his Church, but he is ready to give her the outlet she wants in the Sisters of Mercy's Convent in Dublin, or the Sisters of Charity's Convent in Paris. He sees it's the work she wants, not the religion. Fill women's minds. . . ."

"My wife read too much," said Simon. "Thank God Mabel does not take to books in the same way."

The doctor smiled. "You share the sentiments of a writer friend of mine." He was searching for a cutting in his pocket book. "Yes, here we are. I took it from the *Leader* a year or so back.

'Women have made an invasion of our legal domain. They write dramas, they write treatises. This is the march of the mind, but where are the dumplings? Does it never strike these delightful creatures that their little fingers were meant to be kissed, not to be inked? Women's proper sphere of activity is elsewhere. Are there not husbands, brothers, friends, lovers, to coddle and console? Are there no stockings to darn, no purses to make, no braces to embroider?'

There you have it, Mr. Digby. Give them the chance of becoming mothers, of working out their woman's destiny. Miss Mabel at Montpellier will go out in society with her mother and there will soon be a husband for her. She is a most attractive young person. She is too much your daughter to be swayed by any Romish nonsense. Marriage will give her balance. Send Miss Mabel abroad. Otherwise I will not answer for the consequences." He closed his black bag and shook hands.

Simon went in again to his daughter. There were candles burning on the mantelpiece though it was midday, and through the closed windows he saw the yellow fog drifting. Mabel looked pale and tired among the frilled pillows. Yes. He would have to do as the doctor advised.

"I shall be taking you back to Montpellier, Mabel," he said. "The doctor says you need the climate."

Angry, bitter, miserable tears filled her eyes. "Papa, I don't want to go. I want to stay here, with you."

"My darling, you couldn't stand the winter." There was a catch in his voice. "I should lose you. So we must go as soon as we can."

"Yes," she assented. If he lost her, he would have no one.

He bought her one of the new circular shawls for the journey, and smiled as she undid the wrappings. He put it around her shoulders and admired the effect. She smiled back at him, anxious to give him pleasure, while her heart was cold within her at the thought of having to live once more in the same house as her mother, the woman who had so wounded him.

"I'll look after Eva for you," she told him. "I will see that she gets taught the truth."

They left the fogs of London, crossed a gray and stormy Channel, and traveled once more south. The familiar places had lost their joyous adventure, there were no happy welcoming arms to look forward to. The line of Mabel's lips became straighter as the station carriage bowled up the streets at last to the house in Montpellier.

Eva was on them like a whirlwind, her eyes sparkling, her curly head tousled. Mabel hugged her. She nodded at Geraldine, acknowledging her existence, then presented a cold cheek to her mother's embrace.

"I will take you to your room," said Mrs. Digby.

"Thank you, Mama," said Mabel. "There's really no need to trouble. I can find my way."

It was the same unhappy life again, though the surface was unruffled. It was easy to be polite when conversation never went below the surface, below the trivialities of everyday. Scrupulous courtesy in outward show was an effective way of cutting her mother to the heart. Why should she be spared when she herself had not spared the happiness of others? Mabel would show her father that he could safely leave her to guard the honor of the family in his absence, and be ready to hand back her trust to him when the winter was over and the summer could take her away again.

Eva spoiled it all. She walked into the drawing room where at one end her mother sat with Geraldine, while her father and Mabel sat together. She took her mother's hand, and steadied herself with Geraldine's hand in her other. Very red, with head thrown back, she suddenly cried out, "Papa, I want to be a Catholic like Mama and Geraldine."

For a moment Simon was silent. Then he burst out in an angry shout. "It's your mother who has put this idea into your head." He rose, towering above the child.

"No, Papa, I've found out for myself that the Catholic religion is the best one."

She was looking at him fearfully yet with a kind of desperate courage. He took several paces up and down the room, glanced furiously at his wife, then flung open the door and walked out.

The next day he announced that he had arranged for Eva to go to the Protestant Academy of Mademoiselle Ronsard. Eva went obediently, head held high. Silence descended again on the family meals and gatherings. It was war with no truce.

Mademoiselle Ronsard did her duty as she knew it; in rustling black bombazine, she taught History as a line of Protestant champions against papal aggression from the time of Paul of Tarsus. Scripture lessons were carefully selective in the light thrown on Doctrine by Calvin. Eva Digby plodded on with her work, keeping her thoughts to herself. She did not like walking round the small garden arm in arm during recess.

"What's that you're wearing around your neck?" asked one of the children one day.

"It's a medal," answered Eva. There was an outcry.

"Mademoiselle Ronsard, Eva Digby's wearing a medal!"

Mademoiselle Ronsard bore down on her. "What is this, Eva? A medal? Of what?"

"Of Our Lady," said Eva simply. She had worn it ever since her illness. She was on the point of telling the mistress all about it when Mademoiselle Ronsard cried out in horror.

"A medal! Of the Virgin! At this school! Your father would be terribly put out! Take it off, child, and give it to me to throw away. A horrid superstitious thing!"

"Certainly not!" cried Eva indignantly.

"Then I must take it off for you," said Mademoiselle Ronsard, bridling.

"You'd better not!" cried Eva indignantly. It was Eva's turn to grow fierce now.

"We'll help you, Mademoiselle Ronsard," clamored the little group of children, currying favor. They closed in on her. Mademoiselle Ronsard put out her hand, but Eva was clasping her precious medal tight in one hand, and struck out at the grasping fingers with the other. A big girl seized her by the dress but she twisted away from her. She felt her hair tugged, her feet trodden on, their hands were all around her, but she broke away and made for the gate. It clanged behind her as she ran blindly down the road and made for home.

"What disgraceful behavior!" said her father sternly when all her iniquity had been reported by Mademoiselle Ronsard.

"If you don't give up this nonsense, I shall have to send you home to England. There will be a good school there that will teach you how to act like a proper Protestant child."

Red-eyed, Eva looked up at him. She shook her curly head.

"You can send me, Papa, if you want to, but you can't make me a proper Protestant child."

He dismissed her coldly, turning over in his mind the advisability of sending her away. Would the doctor say of her, too, that her constitution was too delicate for life in England? Suddenly he felt defeated. What was the good of trying to save this brand from burning? Eva had chosen her mother. He was rejected. Let her mother look after her. The child could be baptized if she would.

The news that Eva was to be allowed to receive instruction in the Catholic faith increased Mabel's resentment against her mother. When Simon Digby returned to England, there was no need for her to promise to be loyal or to affirm her Protestantism. Their two hearts beat together and their minds were one. Mabel's politeness to her mother grew more frigid. Geraldine took her to task. "Why can't you be as nice as you are when you are out with friends?" she asked.

"They have not ruined our family happiness," retorted Mabel.

"But Mama has done such a lot for you."

"And Papa has done such a lot for her."

"If only you would read a bit about the Catholic Church."

"Thank you. That is just what I have done. There is quite a lot about it also in the Book of Revelations . . . If you would only read some more."

"If you would only come into a church, I could show you it isn't as bad as what you think."

"I'd rather die than set foot in one of your churches," Mabel said furiously. "Do you hear? I will never cross the threshold of a church."

44

II · Sudden Splendor
1853-1864

Chapter Eight

1853

A T Christmas, Louise de Peignerolles had gone to consult the Mistress General of the Convent of the Sacred Heart at Montpellier, where she had been at school.

"Why, of course you must go on. What else delights Our Lord's Heart but to be asked for the things that to us seem impossible? What else do His great promises to Blessed Margaret Mary mean?" the nun asked her.

"But," said Louise de Peignerolles disconsolately, "Mabel is like granite. She hasn't changed in the least for all my prayers and penances. She is Protestantism personified. And I had such high hopes."

"I . . . I . . . what about God? In September you thought you were never going to see her again. Well, God is master over germs and fogs. And here she is back once more in this City of Mary. But, my dear child, you mustn't be alone in your fight for her soul. Get some of your companions to join you. I will ask the prayers of the nuns here. God will do the rest."

When the door of the Convent closed behind her, Louise already felt better. She began laying her plans and putting them into action. Sidonie and Eugénie joined her at once, Aimée and Geraldine were let into the plot, Laure Langlois and Desirée Bourdaloue made up a mystic Seven. The program was simplicity itself: unremitting prayer to Our Lord's

Sacred Heart with confidence, everything placed in the hands of Our Lady; on their part, fasts, mortifications and the offering of serious, even if small, acts of character training. Like a commander-in-chief, Louise kept her men up to their task, writing reminders to them, suggesting extra efforts, inventing new ways of doing unpleasant things for the great intention. When Eva won her right to instruction, Louise felt that victory for Mabel was just around the corner.

She accosted the older sister. "Very soon you will be a Catholic like us!"

Mabel's blue eyes turned steelily toward her. "Never!"

"But you know, Mabel, it's the one ark of salvation. Our Lord said, 'Thou art Peter and upon this rock I will found my Church.' "

The apologetics of school days were all ready to be poured out, all so perfectly convincing.

" 'By their fruits ye shall know them . . . do men gather figs of thorns and grapes of thistles?' Look what the Catholic Church has done to our happy home," said Mabel in cold, level tones. Before her unflinching gaze Louise's words froze on her lips. Mabel went on with her cross-stitch as though she was alone. Louise faltered and fled, seeking Geraldine for comfort.

"Never mind, Louise. Don't lose hope . . . but don't try that way of attack again. Mabel's head is too full of Protestant arguments and her will can be like iron. No, I think the same as Mama. Only God can touch the depths of her soul."

Light broke suddenly into Louise's thoughts. "Why then," she cried out, "let's put her face to face with the Blessed Sacrament. He will win the victory."

Geraldine shook her head. "For that she would have to go into a church, and that she will never do."

Never? What else delights Our Lord's Heart but to be asked for the things that to us seem impossible? Louise went away, hugging her inspiration to herself. What did it matter if the English Geraldine thought it a mad scheme? She, Louise de Peignerolles, belonged to the Eldest Daughter of the Church, of the race that had produced a Blessed Margaret Alacoque and a Mother Barat. Sacred Heart of Jesus, I trust in You.

The Bishop of Montpellier received Eva into the Church on February 2nd. Only Mabel's studied politeness to her mother cast a shadow on the child's happiness.

Coming out of the Church of Notre Dame des Tables, Louise de Peignerolles stopped to read a notice. A band of singers from the Pyrenees was coming to the neighborhood to give recitals of church music. That would be very interesting.

"I've heard them in Béarn," said Sidonie de Castelbajac, reading over her shoulder. "They sing for devotion only, and only in churches. There are sixty of them. Half sing the words and the other half produce the accompaniment through their half-closed lips. I've never heard anything like it anywhere else. It's really rather impressive. We must go, if you're interested in music."

Louise seized her arm, squeezing it in sudden excitement.

"Yes, I am and so is Mabel Digby. Oh, Sidonie, this is the way to get her into a church to see Our Lord face to face. Look, we'll just talk to everyone about these mountaineers, and then arrange to go and hear them. You see, she'll come out of sheer curiosity."

The Pyrenean choir was a huge success. They were the talk of all Montpellier. Everyone went to hear them, everyone except Mabel Digby. Louise watched her face alight with interest as her companions hummed the airs and tried to reproduce the peculiar accompaniment, but day after day passed and still she shrugged off any invitation to hear the men herself.

"I'm getting desperate," Louise told Sidonie. "There's only one concert more and that's on the 17th, the day after tomorrow."

"Count yourself beaten, my poor dear," said Sidonie. "You'll have to find another way."

"Listen," said Louise, "I'm not beaten. This wants a bit of organizing, but we'll do it. You must arrange a walk with the others and Mabel, and we'll time it to finish near the church just at Benediction time, and then just by accident as it were we'll make a sort of flanking movement around Mabel and she'll be inside the church with us before she has time to realize what's happening."

"Is that all?" asked Sidonie, ironically.

"Oh, no," said Louise in great earnestness. "I shall get my mother to pray, and the seven of us must spend all tomorrow fasting and wearing out our knees with prayer. Our Lady must play her part, too. It's her church we're getting Mabel into."

"Do you know," said Sidonie, surprised out of herself, "I think there's something in your idea."

Madame de Peignerolles and Madame de Castelbajac entered into the plan. In the afternoon of the 17th, the February sun shone warmly in a tender blue sky. There was laughter and joking as the little group of young girls and their mothers set out on their walk. They left the town and took the road to the woodlands where the green was already covering the trees with fresh verdure. From time to time Louise surreptitiously turned her watch to see how time had passed. She led them a circuitous route until at the end of two hours they were facing the roofs of Montpellier and the fields gave way to streets and they found themselves caught in a flood of people moving all in one direction toward the great Church of Notre Dame des Tables while the air shook with the clash of bells. The big doors were wide open, the crowds closing in as they passed through. Louise felt her heart beating violently as she cried out, "Oh, it's the last concert of the Mountaineers. Quick, let's get in and hear them for the last time."

She had hold of Mabel's arm. Behind and to the sides the

Seven closed their ranks. They jostled their way through, taking no notice of their captive, intent on finding a place as high up the aisle as they could. There was very little room inside but they seized chairs and prie-dieu and in spite of some black looks planted them full in view of the altar. Mabel sat down immediately on a chair, with Geraldine on one side and Madame de Peignerolles on the other. Behind in a half circle knelt the other six.

Sidonie thought, "I can do no more. I am dry as an old boot. I feel this is Your turn now, dear Lord."

There was a guttering candle on the High Altar that leaned drunkenly sideways. The noise of the famous choir seemed to her uncouth and unintelligible. The smell of the incense was sickly. An altar boy was wearing a cotta with a great rent in the heavy crochet edging. She watched as though with Protestant eyes the progress of the old women pushing their way through the fidgety throng to collect sous for prie-dieu. She was detached from it all, a spectator only. She had done all she could.

Louise knelt where she could see Mabel's face. It was set in a half-contemptuous fixity, her back defiantly upright as she sat in the midst of the kneeling people. She did not stir as the Bishop came out and the service began. The famous mountaineers might have been a choir of angels but Louise would not have heard them.

"She is here," she prayed. "Dear Lord, she is here. Touch her heart. Convert her."

Mabel's face remained impassive, the blue eyes inscrutable beneath the straight black brows, the mouth steady and unsmiling. At the altar, the server rang the bell for the Benediction as the Bishop raised the monstrance. There was a forward movement like the waves on a still sea as every head bent for the blessing. Louise saw Mabel stiffen in protest. "Jesus, Jesus! Show yourself, Jesus, for this soul!" Louise could pray no more as she hid her face in her hands. At the third ringing, she looked up. Her heart stood still. Before her, Mabel slipped from her chair on to her knees. Her hands went to her heart as though it beat too fast for her breast to hold it, her face, turned toward the altar, was lit with a strange radiance, while great tears rolled silently down her cheeks from eyes that gazed and gazed.

Geraldine had noticed what had happened, too. Sidonie suddenly felt the warmth of happy tears in her eyes. Silent and beside themselves with joy, the Seven stayed on, while the Bishop's procession left the Sanctuary, and the candles were put out, and the mountaineers went back to their heights, and the crowds moved noisily away to their evening meal. Mabel did not change her position, oblivious of all around her. When the church had emptied, Madame de Peignerolles rose and motioned to the others to go away. Geraldine waited a few minutes, then whispered, "Mabel, I think we must go home. Mama will be worried."

Slowly Mabel rose to her feet and followed Geraldine to the door. There was sunlight outside the dimness of the porch. She laid her hand on Geraldine's arm and said, "Geraldine, I am a Catholic."

Out into the same sunlight walked Geraldine. She must be reasonable at all costs.

"You don't know enough, Mabel. You must wait until you understand more of our holy truths before you say you are a Catholic. I think you'd better not say anything to Mama until later. She's not well and it wouldn't do her good to be told something you will be sorry about later."

Mabel stopped, full in the evening sunlight. Her voice was steady and slow and all her heart went into her words.

"Geraldine, I am a Catholic. Jesus Christ has looked at me. I shall not change."

The soft light of the lamp fell that night on the heads of the

52

two sisters bent over one book. In low tones, lest they should awake the household, Geraldine read each article of faith from Bossuet's *Exposition of Christian Doctrine.* Mabel listened to each, then laid her hand simply on the book and said, "I believe."

The midnight chimes struck, but the work was not finished. As the first lightening of the sky came, the last dogma was reached, and Mabel made her last act of faith. Geraldine closed the book. There was nothing more to be said.

In the morning Mabel knocked at her mother's door. Surprised, Mrs. Digby saw her frigid daughter drop on her knees beside her, facing her candidly while she told her that she, too, would be a Catholic, begging forgiveness for her long months of coldness and anger. Mrs. Digby's arms went around her, and their two loves, so long sundered, ran together in joy that was beyond words.

Monsignor Thibaud saw Mabel the same day. Hearing her story and seeing for himself the limpid faith that was hers, he felt the hand of God very near. She must have some further instruction, but he himself would have the honor of receiving her. On March 19th, the Feast of St. Joseph, he poured the waters of baptism on the head of Mary Josephine Mabel Digby. The next day she received from him the Bread of Life, and the strength of the Holy Spirit.

"What did she see?" asked Louise of Sidonie.

"She won't say. I mean, I don't think anyone has been indiscreet enough to ask her. Or there's a sort of reserve that keeps you off the subject. Our Lord looked at her. I suppose it was like His looking at St. Peter after his fall. . . ."

"Or perhaps she saw Him like St. Paul on the road to Damascus. Well, it'll be her secret. But it's very wonderful."

"Oh, Louise, yes. It is wonderful . . . but I was thinking of poor Mr. Digby." Louise felt suddenly sick. Her responsibility was stark before her, inescapable. His misery at the loss of this dearest of daughters cut her like a knife. The pain of the world surged up around her, pain her action had helped to bring about, and she shrank from its reality. Why had he to suffer? It seemed brutal, cruel. There was only one justification for it, incontrovertible only because Truth itself had said, "Do not think I came to send peace upon earth. I came not to send peace but the sword, to set a man at variance against his father . . . he that loveth father or mother more than Me is not worthy of Me."

Even now there was a letter traveling across France to England to tell Simon Digby that into the world of trains and steamships, factories and general evolutionary progress, the Finger of God had stretched and touched his daughter irrevocably.

Chapter Nine

1856

A s the train rattled and clanged its smoky way across the smiling valley of the Loire, Mrs. Digby faced defeat. Opposite her, neat in her plain traveling costume, Mabel sat with folded hands, looking out of the window. What was she seeing? The green hillsides and flowering trees, the sparkle of the sun on the waters, the little villages or the embowered château rising above? Or had her thoughts leaped ahead to the streets of Paris and Notre Dame and the great orator Father Felix and the momentous judgment he would be asked to make? They had nothing to say to each other, each busy with her thoughts.

Mrs. Digby went over the events of the past three years, trying to see more clearly the pattern running through them, trying to see that pattern shaping with definite lines in the future. There were those first happy days in the spring of 1853 when her daughter had been given back to her, and together they had prepared to face the wrath of Simon, happiness shot through with keen joy in a new intimacy with God, and keen dread of the pain they were inflicting. Then the surprise of finding that, once the shock was over, family life could be resumed, with its round of visits and entertaining and expeditions into the country. True, there must be no talk of religion, true that, though Mabel and her father rode abroad together, there was a barrier between them, and she caught from time to time a look of unsatisfied longing in the eyes of father and daughter when the veil was lifted for a moment. But when they had left Montpellier for the mild climate of Touraine, and had taken a house in Tours, the strain and stress were left behind, and life seemed to spread out again smoothly, with all the richer joy of days caught up into the purpose of eternity.

Mrs. Digby had sent Eva to the school of the Sacred Heart nuns at Marmoutier, and she and her other two daughters had been received as Children of Mary and went to their meetings at the old Abbey. Mabel had joined the school retreat, given by Father Barelle. Was that the initial mistake? At the end, she had come home and asked to join the Society. Simon had been wild with fury, but she herself was beside him, this time. It was folly to think of such a thing. Mabel was too young, and too young a Catholic, to know what she was about. The doctors who were caring for her health laughed at the idea and said she could never stand the strain.

Mrs. Digby went over again what Father Barelle had said. Mabel was one in a thousand. She had mental gifts, a will of iron, a power of sympathy and tenderness that were allied to a generous longing to give. She was destined surely to exert a great influence in the world. In the world. Yes, perhaps like Eugénie de Montijo, who had made a love match with Louis Napoleon and was now Empress of France. The young count who asked for Mabel's hand was admirable in every way, cultured, pious, very much in love. Mrs. Digby smiled for a moment as she remembered how Geraldine and Mabel had endeavored to make themselves unattractive, wearing plain dark dresses and scraping their hair back flat against their faces. Perhaps even this unworldliness had a charm for the young man. He was willing to wait, had waited now three years, with unabated love. But then so had Mabel.

As though it was yesterday, Mrs. Digby saw the bright June sunlight on the old cobbled street in Tours where at an upper window in their house, they had watched the Corpus Christi procession, their first procession as believers. The long file of choristers passed below, straggling as they sang, then into sight came the canopy, with the priest beneath bearing the Body of the Lord. The crowd thronging the street knelt, and, as the monstrance drew nearer, the shreds of hope seemed to be torn from her mother's heart and the stark certainty of what God was asking left her in agony. She caught a glimpse of twinkling candles, of blue incense rising below the window, as they all fell on their knees. The Lord was passing. "Are you still thinking of becoming a nun?" she had suddenly whispered to Mabel. "Yes."

"Think no more of it until you are twenty-one."

She saw now that that was the first step to victory for her daughter. She would not see it at the time, and, when they had bought the old Château de Chatigny just outside Tours, she had drowned that momentary certainty of her mother's instinct in all the busy, full life of the châtelaine. And life had been good. Simon had even made friends with the Archbishop, and had no objection to one of the turret rooms being made into a chapel where the Blessed Sacrament was reserved. Mabel and Geraldine were happy sacristans, and it was good to pray there, as though in a little fortress, looking out on to the dark pine woods. Mabel had another of the turret rooms for her own. Mrs. Digby remembered the laughing comment of a friend, "Why, it's as simple as a Carmelite cell!" and the surprise of another who had found Mabel's dispensary, where she prepared remedies for the poor. Strange that that should have given her reassurance.

She had told herself that Mabel was playing with two mutually destructive vocations. It was all very well for her and Charlotte Leslie, whose family had also settled in Tours, to spend time in the Carmelites' Chapel, dreaming of a life of contemplation. The next thing she would hear would be of Mabel's helping the Sisters of Charity in their hospital, learning from them how to treat ringworm and skin diseases that would have sickened the average young lady. The Sisters had something practical to give. The papers had spoken of the good nursing aid they were giving to Miss Florence Nightingale at Scutari. Mabel's interest and skill in nursing would find proper instructors. But she could not be both Mary and Martha. Besides, there was the example of M. Dupont, whom everyone was now calling the Holy Man of Tours. He had married, and married life had not prevented his reaching high sanctity. Mabel had looked with him at the lovely head of Christ Suffering enshrined in his drawing room, she had seen the stream of people passing through to honor that Holy Face in reparation for blasphemy, and in her presence he had cured a crippled child. Tall and venerable, easy and cultured in his conversation, well-dressed and neat, he pointed the way to an ordinary quiet holiness that had nothing outrageous or uncouth about it. So could Mabel be, when she had married and become a happy mother of many children.

And yet, and yet . . . The two years had passed, and April

7th, 1856 had come. When the festivities were over, Mabel had come to her again. Father Belfour was to give a retreat at Marmoutier. Could she go? She wanted another opinion. Why not? Mrs. Digby had seen the doctor again and had his diagnosis of a threatened consumption that only care could avert. She had taken the precaution also of seeing Father Belfour before the retreat. He had interviewed Mabel at the Château de Chatigny. "During the course of the retreat you must remain alone with God . . . and me. You must not speak to any of the nuns." Of course Mabel was loyal, but she was frank, too, with the priest. He had heard all her arguments, had seen that Mary and Martha would both be satisfied if she entered the Society of the Sacred Heart. He had declared, "Your vocation to the religious life is certain, supernatural, clear as the sun at noonday. It is equally clear that you must give it up . . . the sacrifice God demands of you . . . go and tell your mother you are at her disposal, for marriage with the Count."

Mrs. Digby remembered Mabel's stricken face when she came home, and told her the priest's decision. To Mabel's agonized, "Will you, Father, take the responsibility of this decision before God?" he had added a firm "I will." But what of her mother's responsibility? She knew, as he did not, of that instantaneous change in her wilful, headstrong daughter after the Benediction in the church at Montpellier. She had felt the finger of God on her daughter as he had not. She had seen all the old proud faults brought under the gentle yoke of Christ when all her lifelong training had proved useless. She had still that stifled certainty that God was asking for her daughter. Yet there was his decision. She would not listen to anything Reverend Mother Bosredont of Marmoutier might say.

The train's wheels were keeping up a monotonous clanking. She felt that she was in the power of something that would go on whatever she might do to try to stop it. God had foiled her satisfaction and shown her each day that her daughter, silent, but unsatisfied, was becoming paler, more easily tired, thinner and more languid. Simon was away in England. He would have only one answer to give if she did consult him. She thought of his fury. She thought of her daughter. Was it really true that you could die of a broken heart? She thought at last of God. Then she had called Mabel to her, and proposed still another opinion. They would both of them go to Paris.

There they would see the celebrated Dr. Bouillet for her health's sake, and Father Felix for the sake of her soul. For a moment Mabel's face had lit up. Had it been a flicker of hope like the last spurt of a dying flame, or was it the reflected light of a searching lantern on the face of a traveler lost in the dark? With each turn of the wheels, they were brought nearer to certainty. But in her heart of hearts Mrs. Digby knew that she was facing defeat.

The next day in Paris they made their way to the Jesuit residence and asked for Father Felix. Mabel's heart sank at the thought of having to tell her story again to an unknown priest, used to the company of all the most distinguished men and women of the day, who were attracted by his oratory in the famous pulpit of Notre Dame. Reverend Mother Bosredont had told her he knew the Society of the Sacred Heart; yes, but he knew it here in Paris where Mabel herself was unknown and unfamiliar with any of the nuns. She glanced across at her mother, so self-assured and imposing. Where would she be, between these two great personalities?

The door of the parlor opened quietly. A little man, with unprepossessingly ugly features, walked in and surveyed them both. A smile lit his face and Mabel suddenly saw its beauty. This was the simple, humble innkeeper's son, and not the great preacher. She felt assured.

"Perhaps Mademoiselle Digby would have the kindness to wait while I speak to her mother first?"

She found herself outside the room. This would be Father

Belfour over again, with her mother getting the first innings. Miserably she awaited her own summons, going over what she could say to the Jesuit. What was there that one could say except that God wanted her, and if He wanted her, presumably He would undertake to give her the strength she needed and would pledge Himself not to let those she loved suffer. After all, what was her love for them in comparison with His love for them? No, there was nothing she could say except that God wanted her and that she longed to give herself to Him, fully, utterly, with no shadow of turning back.

The door reopened. Father Felix beckoned her in. His shrewd eyes watched her kindly. Then he spoke.

"Your call to the religious life is supernatural and as evident as can be." He paused. Mabel glanced despairingly at him. So it was to be Father Belfour over again. She saw eyes that smiled down into hers, as he said, "You wish to enter the Sacred Heart. Meet me therefore at the Hôtel Biron next Friday."

She turned quickly to her mother. Mrs. Digby nodded assent. Of course her mother's great heart would not act meanly. Mabel's pale face broke into smiles as she stammered her thanks to Father Felix.

Mother Prévost, Assistant-General and superior of the Convent in the absence of Reverend Mother Barat, saw life with unsentimental eyes. Her memory went back to the horror of the slaves' revolt in San Domingo, and the hazards of her escape with her father in 1792, to the sight of the head of the Princess de Lamballe aloft on a pike and the raucous shouts of the crowd drunk with blood, to the secret underground existence of friends and relations ready to face the guillotine rather than lose their faith. She had seen the new beginnings perilously built up again on the foundations of the martyrs, and the renewed attacks of the world, the flesh and the devil. She knew that there was a war in progress.

God's warriors must have no pretense about them. Her seventy-two years were bending her shoulders, and slowing her walk, but her spirit was as firm and militant as ever. She was glad to learn from Father Felix's note that he had a new postulant to offer her. Soon she would have finished her course, and there must be others to carry on God's warfare. With pleasurable anticipation she laid her hand on the door of the parlor in the Hôtel Biron, and opened the door.

She sat watching her visitors while Father Felix explained the case. An exquisitely beautiful mother, dressed in impeccable taste that bespoke wealth and position, perhaps somewhat overwhelming; very self-assured with the natural self-assurance that does not question itself; obviously cultured, with ideas of her own and perhaps imposing those ideas unconsciously on others. The daughter, small in comparison with the mother, pale, delicate-looking, with a mouth that might very well mean obstinacy; silent while the priest and her mother spoke; acquiescent in what they said, advancing no opinion herself; one of a family of daughters whose future this masterful mother no doubt was planning for them. It was fitting that one should be a religious in gratitude for the gift of the faith, but fittingness did not mean a call from God. Converts: they had much to learn; first fervor was to be distrusted. She put a question here and there as the tale was unfolded. Mother and priest had done. They were waiting now, all three, for her answer. She was aware of a steady pair of blue eyes fixed on her. She found herself avoiding their direct gaze, though her words were for the girl more than for the other two.

"After all that I have heard, you are totally unsuited for our Society. Forgive my frankness when I say that we have enough of your type of convert who give little hope of perseverance and are so little instructed in their religion. And

61

then, you have no health. We have already so many in our infirmaries."

Her words fell into an abyss of silence. At length Father Felix spoke.

"But Reverend Mother, will you not leave one little loophole of hope?"

Mother Prévost folded her hands. She had caught the almost irate movement of the mother at her refusal. Could they not see that her answer was the kinder for its very bluntness, that she would not hurt the girl by holding out illusory hopes? She had been surprised at her own unwonted harshness, but the words had been spoken and to soften them now would be cruel. She would not be persuaded into accepting the girl against all better judgment.

"I should not be fair either to our Society or to you if I held out any false hopes. I am sorry, but I could not take the responsibility."

There was nothing further to be said. Mrs. Digby rose, and, accompanied by Father Felix, still in a state of stupefied surprise, left the convent. Mabel walked beside them down the drive to the street. The dome of Les Invalides appeared above the trees, carriages with well-dressed men and women were bowling down the boulevards in the sunshine. She felt numb, astonished by the reply she had received, bewildered by its unexpectedness.

"Yet You promised me, Lord," she kept repeating to herself. "You promised me."

As the train rattled its way across the garden of France, back to Touraine and the Château de Chatigny and the happy prospect of undisturbed family life once more, Mrs. Digby was facing defeat. But this time she would not admit it. Somehow, with the help of God, Mabel should get what God wanted her to have.

Chapter Ten

1856

H I s Eminence held the boiled egg between his fingers and deftly struck off the top with his spoon. There was a simplicity in an egg cooked *à la coque* that pleased him more than banquets when he had to be the guest of honor. *A la coque!* The simple name of the notary's daughter who from her Burgundian convent two centuries before had set the world on fire. Simple things were never as disappointing as complicated ones. They had a strength that was unassailable. What more simple and more strong than that God should show His love for men in the human Heart of His Only Begotten Son? Margaret Alacoque had been God's simple instrument in strengthening men with an unshakable trust in the power of His Sacred Heart.

What a lot France owed to that Heart! He thought of Jesuit devotion, of the springing up of so much in the last fifty years since the storm of the Revolution had died away, fostered by the returning Sons of St. Ignatius. Then there was humble Mother Barat who had placed all her confidence in the Sacred Heart when she had gone up from Burgundy to Paris some fifty years past, and now her nuns were all over France and beyond. He was glad that they were here in his diocese, almost within sight of his episcopal palace, teaching the rising generation what God had meant about His love for His creatures.

A sound of laughter arose from the great room beneath his. Some of his hundred and fifty pensioners. He was glad the floods from the Loire had sent him these unfortunates to look after. Perhaps in his small way he could teach them something of the Fatherhood of God. Another gale of laughter . . . what a lightening of the spirit when one had lost all except the bare necessities, and enough food and clothes and a roof over one's head were assured! Only their poor shepherd in the room above, crushing the empty egg shell on his plate, must bear, like all superiors, the daily burden, temporal and spiritual, of his flock. Well, God could crush all his difficulties as easily as the broken fragments of an egg *à la coque*. He rose and went to his study for the morning's work.

There Mrs. Digby found him. He listened quietly while she told him of Mother Prévost's refusal.

"You do not see in this the finger of God, Mrs. Digby?"

She shook her head. "Alas, Your Eminence, no. I can see now with open eyes that with the gift of faith in the church at Montpellier, my daughter received a vocation, a love of suffering, and an insight into the life that is lived within with Our Lord. I remember too clearly now what her godmother said to her on the day of her baptism, when she gave her a crucifix: 'You can never love Him enough. He is the only One to be loved without danger.' I should sin against the light if I denied this."

Cardinal Morlot nodded. "The call is simple. I have seen it ever since I made your daughter's acquaintance. Only the road to it is complicated. What of her father?"

"Your Eminence, you know him. . . ."

"And appreciate more than I can say his straightforwardness, and his high principles. He is in perfect good faith. . . ."

"He has said that the day Mabel enters a convent, he will leave the house for ever."

"Does not that give you pause?"

She twisted her hands in her lap, then answered, "Your Eminence, if it is God's Will, I can do my husband no service by refusing to accept it."

The cardinal nodded again. "There must be trust in God, when the Loire runs in her channel and when she bursts her banks. You are right, Mrs. Digby. A priest said of your daughter, 'She is a Spartan, a heroic soul. She has a will of iron, but it is a will that never refuses anything that God may ask.' His wisdom marks out the way. Our next step, then, is to change the mind of His instruments."

"I shall approach Reverend Mother Bosredont at Marmoutier," said Mrs. Digby.

"And I shall write to Reverend Mother Barat in Paris," said Monsignor, thinking, "The simplest way may be the strongest."

Mother Bosredont had often watched Mabel Digby at the meetings of the Children of Mary. She had heard the laughter that came from the group where she was the center; she had seen her immediately after in the chapel with eyes fixed on the tabernacle. Never for a minute had she doubts about Mabel's suitability for the religious life. Health? She could do a great deal when her mind was set on helping the poor or nursing the sick. If the doctors would let the girl alone, she would win through. To learn that Mabel had been refused by Mother Prévost came like a bombshell.

"Mrs. Digby, you are one of our Children of Mary. So is your daughter. Our Lady's Motherhood means something real. Ask her. Ask her through her Immaculate Conception."

Mother Bosredont was thinking, "Not two years since Pius IX promulgated that as a dogma. Our Lady will welcome the chance of showing she loves our filial appreciation of that." Aloud she added, "I shall approach the Mother House in Paris and give them a fuller account of your daughter."

Seventy-seven years had brought ripe wisdom to Reverend Mother Barat, a wisdom that went straight to the Source of all wisdom. At her desk, so close to the chapel, decisions could be reached that overleaped human reasoning. But prudence caught up with intuition and she made fuller inquiries about Mabel Digby. The Paris doctor was reassuring. A winter in such a place as Hyères would probably establish her health sufficiently. She liked better Mother Bosredont's latest letter. "The young English girl has a soul highly gifted for prayer and withal an astonishing humility and childlike obedience. She is charming." Miss Mabel Digby could try her vocation. But she should enter not in the Paris noviceship at Conflans, but in Marmoutier. Mother Prévost did not shake her head in pessimistic disapproval; she knew too well the ways of saints.

The Mediterranean waves danced blue through September and October. From the house they had taken at Hyères, the Digby family could see the rocky shore and, in the distance behind, the mountains moving down from the Alps to the Corniche. Eva was still at school, but Kenelm came from time to time, holidaying from his work in England, and Essex, proud of his commission in the Queen's Army, spent his furloughs with Geraldine, Mabel and their mother. Only Simon Digby was absent. True to his threat, he had not set foot in the house since they had made known Mabel's decision. She had not yet entered. He would wage a war of attrition.

"Of course," said Kenelm one evening as they sat and watched the sun sink in splendor over the waters, "I don't approve of what Mabel is going to do. I just don't understand why a good-looking girl like her should shut herself up for life. But fundamentally it's her own life that's in question and she has a right to dispose of it as she likes. It's putting all her eggs into one basket, and she runs the risk of smashing the lot."

"So you do in marriage," said Geraldine, wishing that she, too, was doing as her younger sister.

"Talking of smashing," said Essex, red in the face in his endeavor to see sense in what was happening, heart breaking while loyalty defended, "why, I may get a bullet in me in the very first action I take part in and then where would be all the care and money spent on bringing me up? Barrack life isn't all beer and skittles, and yet none of you makes the same fuss about my enduring that as you do about Mabel's living in a convent. I bet convents can give points to barracks. Anyhow, I think it's a bit heroic wanting to shut yourself up all your life to serve God. If you met it in a novel about someone who did it for his king or even for his lover, you'd all be weeping with sentiment."

Geraldine said, "You don't understand. It's not shutting yourself up. It's opening out your horizons, getting away from the narrow outlook of the town and climbing those mountains to get a terrific view out over the sea."

Kenclm laughed. "You've a lot of hard walking without much of a view on the lower slopes of a mountain, my dear Geraldine. Still, I am quite prepared to admit that Mabel's very much better since she made up her mind. She's got pink in her cheeks again and she's riding her horse like an Amazon, and she kept me in fits of laughter the other day with some nonsense. Yes, she's certainly happier . . . only I sometimes think happiness is very fragile."

"Like eggs," Essex added. "The wisest thing to do with them is to let them hatch."

Mrs. Digby took her children everywhere with her. There were dances and soirées and expeditions into the country. It was all very pleasant, and she found herself clinging to these last days, illusively promising her a permanence of joy in watching Mabel's ease in society and in receiving her straightforward sympathy in the things that really mattered. They returned after Christmas to the Château de Chatigny. Reverend Mother Bosredont asked her to fix a day for Mabel's entry. When she had recovered from her cold, her trousseau was not yet ready, there was a chance that her father might be coming to France; Essex was on the last days of his leave. There was always some good reason why she should not go yet.

Mrs. Digby went into Tours and entered the cathedral. After a morning's shopping, she would go to confession before returning home. She entered the Cardinal's confessional, and ran through her usual list of faults and failings, and waited for the absolution. There was a pause. The voice behind the grille sounded severe.

"And how long are you going to keep God waiting, Madame?"

"I am ready, Your Eminence."

"Then take your daughter to the Sacred Heart."

The absolution followed. She felt strangely happy again. God was holding out His Hand and supporting her now in all His fullness of strength. She needed Him. In the next week the post brought her a legal document from her husband. It was a deed of separation.

The moist earth was beginning to stir with fresh green life that 19th of February when Mabel stole around the room of the château in the early morning by herself. A stair squeaked with a familiar recurrence that caught at her heart. There would be other feet, in future, on that stair. She took a last look at the pine trees from her own turret window, knelt for the last time in the little chapel where others would now set things in order for her Lord, opened the cupboard door where her cordials for the poor were ranged in neat order, saw the breakfast table laid with her place as never again, walked through the smiling group of servants in the kitchen who knew nothing of where she was going, and out to the stables. The groom was not there and she opened the door herself. Her own horse was in the corner box. He stirred uneasily as she drew near, as though sensing something untoward. She laid her hand on his neck, and he shook his head, then bent down. For a moment, all the grief she had stifled seemed to gather to a head, the sorrow she must not show to others lest her resolution and theirs should be weakened. She saw again days of happy intimacy with her father. Never again would they ride out together, nor their minds journey side by side. There was a wound that could only be healed when they looked both with unclouded eyes at God. In time or in eternity? Here and now, time crept by with all the slowness of eternity. One last hug, and she went out from the stable with never a backward look.

Mrs. Digby ordered the carriage and saw to the placing of Mabel's trunk. Together they drove off down the road until at a turn the château was lost to sight. The horse's hoofs beat out regularly the miles that lay between, until the great gateway of Marmoutier came into view. The wooden doorway was wide open, and they passed under the old stone arch and swept around to the front door. Mother Bosredont was waiting for them on the steps. Mrs. Digby held her daughter in a last embrace, then handed her to the nun. A deep-toned clock struck twelve. Mabel whispered, "The hour of the Crucifixion." She went inside and the portress shut the door.

They were all waiting for her within to show her the way about the enclosure, her cell, the refectory, the way to the chapel, the places to put her belongings in. Mabel listened while her heart followed her mother in her lonely drive back to the Château de Chatigny. By three they had finished and left her alone to find her way to the chapel. It was the hour of the "Consummatum est," this Friday of February, and in agony and triumph she felt united to the great Sacrifice of Christ. He was there on the altar, taking all sorrow into His Redemptive Life.

"Sister!"

She looked up with tearful eyes. A young nun was waiting beside her. "Will you have the kindness to do a little supervision in the school?" Evidently it was a request that demanded acquiescence. Mabel rose and followed her out. In silence, which the nun did not seem disposed to break, they went along the corridor until they reached a room through whose closed doors sounds of merriment were breaking. Mabel felt a small wooden clapper thrust into her hand.

"Give the signal when you get in, and say the *Veni Sancte.*"

The door was opened and shut. Mabel was inside and the nun had gone. There seemed to be needlework bags all over the place and pieces of calico hawked around. Some twenty girls, demure in black overalls, were staring at her, taking in this new little English postulant, no taller than the tallest of them. In all the cruelty of their twelve years, they saw her red eyes, her plain black dress, the unbecoming way her hair was done, and they nudged each other with smiles. Mabel's finger found the hinge of the wooden clapper and she slipped the two sides together. The sound was not expertly made but it was enough to bring the class to their knees. They waited. Mabel's mind was a blank. How did the *Veni Sancte* go? No words, Latin, French or English, came to her lips. The silence seemed endless. There were glances from one to another of the girls, and someone rose and thrust a book under her nose. In the front row, a black-eyed child turned around with the malicious helpfulness that is the first step to outrage, and cried out, "The nun always says the prayer!"

Not a second of hesitation. "With me, the prayer will be recited by the best behaved child," said Mabel, and the book was handed by her direction to a chubby staid child who knelt demurely. There was silence again as the prayer was said. Mabel's fingers mercifully found the knack of the signal, and they all rose and sat down again at their desks. She smiled at them. Surprisingly they were waiting to be told what to do.

She selected her monitress, and the work began. They were still watching her, appraising her excellent French and her skill to help them in the mysteries of run and fell seams. Cécile, the pert-tongued, was silent, intent on her hem.

"Born to rule," commented the young nun to the mistress general as they passed an hour later.

Chapter Eleven

1857—1859

C É C I L E twiddled the button of her glove in and out of its buttonhole and moved from foot to foot. Nothing so exciting as this had happened since the floods of nearly two years ago. Waiting in the long corridor outside the chapel, she could see a good deal already. There were important looking visitors arriving. She would like to wear a bustle if she could be as beautiful and stately as Mrs. Digby, just sweeping in through the door with Miss Geraldine beside her. Mother Bournonville was getting the children now into their final ranks, the littlest behind with their hair beneath their white veils, brushed glossy by the Sisters, the Blue Ribbons in front looking very good and proper; they were keeping what Mother Bournonville called "custody of the eyes." Their Postulant was going to get the habit. They, the Third Division, had decided that she would not be long in getting it. She made them work and you couldn't tell what she was thinking. Not like Mother Bournonville, who would certainly send the Third Division away if they asked her any question at this excruciating moment. The Mistress of Discipline was casting a last sergeant-major look over her children: every veil hanging correctly, every glove buttoned, every white-braided merino dress at the right height above the ankles.

The dozens of candles on the altar were now shining as the servers moved away with their tapers. Mother Perlin was playing soft inviting tunes at the organ. A light clap of the signal and the big girls of the First Class, with their blue ribbons crossed over their shoulders and hanging down their sides, walked at a slow and measured pace into the chapel, up the middle aisle, around with an ordered genuflection in front of the top bench, then down the side and into their places, with the school following their lead. It was exciting to find a carpet up the middle aisle, just as though it was a first-class feast. Cécile thrilled to find herself in an inside place with an uninterrupted view up to the solitary prie-dieu before the altar steps.

Now Mother Perlin was rousing the organ to more martial tones. The Cardinal, in his Roman purple, had come to the altar. But the organ pealed on, and Cécile turned to see what was happening at the bottom of the chapel. Yes, there was the Mother Assistant with ceremonial black gloves on, leading by the hand their Postulant. How lovely she looked in white bridal array, with a long white train hanging from her shoulders, a white veil, and a wreath of white roses on her brown hair, dark against the whiteness! She was kneeling now on the white prie-dieu, and the nuns were all singing the *Veni Creator Spiritus,* and the Holy Spirit was brooding over the chapel.

There was a rustle as the visitors in front, the children in the benches, and the nuns in the stalls at the side sat down. His Eminence had risen and was giving the sermon. Cécile could not follow it all, what with being agog to see what was going to happen next, and what with that sense of God's

Truth and Love having come right down into Marmoutier at the prayer of His creatures. Somehow He was there, watching like her all the simple pageantry, infusing into it something that was not just outward show. "God's special choice—," the Cardinal was saying. Cécile saw their Postulant's bent head. They knew she didn't like compliments. Well, the last words were said now, and the Cardinal moved along to the end of the altar rail.

The school sat up with fresh interest as he stood beside the basket containing the neatly folded religious garments. Their Postulant had risen and was kneeling at the rails while the Cardinal sprinkled the habit with holy water and said the prayers. Cécile knew what they were. Mother Bournonville had explained them the night before at recreation. He was reminding God, most faithful in His promises of eternal good things and most sure in their fulfillment, that He had promised to His faithful the raiment of salvation and the robe of everlasting happiness. In His kindness He would bless the black habit, which meant humility of heart and contempt of the world, a vesture of holy chastity, and then their Postulant, clothed on earth in hallowed raiment, would hereafter be given, as a garment, a blessed immortality.

Now it was the turn of the veil, on to which God was invited to pour the abundant strength of His blessing, "so that it might make His servant who wore it, in all things subject to Him, preserving in her true humility, and restraining the eyes of her heart from all vanity." Reverend Mother and the Mother Assistant were beside Mabel Digby now. The folded white veil was placed on her head, hiding the roses, and the nuns opened it out over the bridal veil. The Cardinal was saying, "Receive the yoke of the Lord, for His yoke is sweet and His burden is light. May the Father and the Son and the Holy Spirit bless thee and exalt thee in holiness and in love and fulfill all thy petitions for ever and ever."

The basket had been handed over to Eva Digby, small for

her fourteen years, fair-haired and matched with another fair-haired child from the school.

Now Mabel had risen and, half hidden in the long novice's white veil, was walking alone down the chapel aisle, with Eva and her companion going ahead with the basket. Cécile, with eyes downcast for a moment, overwhelmed by a sudden glimpse of the tremendous things the Cardinal had promised their Postulant, saw her white-slippered feet pass. How thankful she would be to kick off those bits of vanity, and show her—what was it?—contempt of the world, bustles and such-like, by wearing the home-made cloth shoes that they saw old Sister Duranthon making in her little shoe shop! Mother Perlin was again playing the organ. The nuns were singing some lovely motets. Cécile gave her attention to the visitors, speculating on who they were who were wiping tears from their eyes. A silly thing, anyhow, when someone had just been promised a garment of blessed immortality.

There was another stir at the back of the chapel. Mabel Digby was returning. Against all Mother Bournonville's recommendations, Cécile turned to watch. She looked like any other nun now in her black habit, with hanging rosary and goffered cap, and white veil framing her face. Her cheeks were flushed a little, her deep blue eyes under their dark brows seemed to see only the altar as she walked up again and knelt on her prie-dieu. The Cardinal began the Mass. At the moment of Communion, Mabel Digby united herself to the Divine Victim whose sacrifice embraced her time-bound offering in His eternal Priesthood.

Now when the Cardinal had left the altar, the nuns were all standing in their stalls. The Mother Assistant had the new novice by the hand and was leading her round to each one to receive the kiss of peace while they intoned the Magnificat. Cécile watched the pleased smile break over the wrinkled face of one of the old nuns as she embraced the young English girl. There did not seem anything very ecclesiastical in the bearhug old Sister Duranthon gave her, but "joy in the presence of the angels of God" came suddenly like a song into Cécile's mind.

It was over. Mother Perlin pulled out all the stops and pealed a triumphant melody as Mabel Digby left the chapel. There was a frou-frou of departing visitors at the top end. Mrs. Digby, looking more queenly than a queen, with a kind of radiance about her, was still kneeling on the prie-dieu as the children filed out. Cécile was filled with wonder. She knew that Mr. Digby was not there, because he disapproved, because he was a Protestant. That must hurt. How queer that you could be at the same time so happy. She twiddled the button off her glove as she walked down the chapel in perplexity. Then for a fleeting moment she broke through the outward pageant of Gothic arch and statues and school benches and choirstalls, and was in that region where the Holy Spirit brooded with intense life. And she knew then that these contradictions could be when we wore only the hallowed raiment of earth, but that there was no hurt when the garments of everlasting happiness were put on.

"Wake up! Cécile," said Mother Bournonville. "There will be classes as usual from ten-thirty."

Classes as usual. That would mean that they would get back their Postulant; only now she would be their Novice. Their Novice. Alas, not for long. Father Felix came to Marmoutier in the course of the summer. The famous orator used his shrewd eyes to some effect and listened attentively to what was said. Back in Paris, he sought out Reverend Mother Barat.

"You have the pearl of all your novices hidden away in Touraine," he told her.

In September of 1857 Reverend Mother Barat sent to Reverend Mother Bosredont and asked that Sister Mabel

Digby should join the rest of the Society's novices at Conflans on the outskirts of Paris.

The Third Division at Marmoutier was heart-broken.

"She made me work without ever scolding me," said Cécile sadly. "I never wanted to be naughty with her. I could have kept my Green Ribbon all the term."

But their Novice had knelt at the feet of a saint and seen kind tired eyes reading her soul in utter simplicity and truth. She had told Reverend Mother Barat the secret of that first great meeting with Christ at Montpellier, she had shown her the grief that separation from her father meant, and they had understood each other. Then she was lost among the seventy other white-veiled novices, living their life, daily learning of the rule, holding in her own hands, as each one held, the possibility of full-hearted correspondence with God's grace to reach heights of holiness or of living a life of mediocre goodness. Two years of noviceship ended in the spring of 1858, two years filled to the brim with happenings worth no chronicler's attention.

In the world outside, by her handling of the Mutiny in India, England had regained the prestige lost in the Crimea. Italy was seething with ideas that threatened soon to take shape in deeds. Conflicting forces gathered in France. There were great problems to worry the statesmen. Within the wall of Conflans, seventy novices were learning the principles on which alone true peace can rest. Looking back on the doings of her noviceship, Mabel saw certain things standing out: her Mother's understanding words, "Give all your confidence now to your superior. It is she who has the right to it now," joy to find that her cousin Marcella Digby and friend Charlotte Leslie had followed her to Conflans, happiness to find so many fervent fellow novices.

Mabel smiled to remember how, in the midst of the preparation of candles for a feast day, she had run into Mother

Goetz and had been told to go straight to bed. She did not feel ill, but this was an opportunity for the unquestioning obedience that St. Ignatius advocated. Meekly she set down the candelabra and retired without a word to Mother Mallac. She saw the sacristan's face as she looked into the cubicle where she had taken to her bed, and her mild reproach, "If you go to bed in the day, you should warn those you are working with. What's the matter?" Her own, "I don't know," sounded so silly. She supposed the order had been meant for someone else, but she had reaped the profit of sounding silly.

She had felt silly, too, when she noticed what long interviews some of the novices seemed to have with the confessor in the confessional. They must be chosen souls, mystics perhaps, at any rate souls who knew something of the interior life. She had made one or two attempts to speak to the priest of her soul, but the words just stuck and he had given her the absolution before she had laid bare her thoughts. Mother Goetz had laughed and said, "Don't worry, Sister. It's because you are a simple soul." There were two things that stood out from her confessions. Father de Ravignon had shattered her complacent avowal of an imperfection not tackled with a brief, "What cowardice!" and Father de Pontlevoy had said mildly, "You will give Holy Church the trouble of canonizing you, will you not?" Holy Church canonized only faithful souls. She determined to be faithful to the least jot and tittle of her Rule. She would never be a great saint unless God overwhelmed her with unlooked-for graces.

Mother Barat was a saint. She had come from the Mother House near Les Invalides to make her retreat at Conflans, where the window overlooked green fields and the mingling of the waters of the Marne and the Seine. One night Mabel had been in the chapel when the little click of an opening door told her that someone was up in the tribune at the back. In the dusk of the chapel the novice was indistinguishable, and before she could move, whispered words of love were breathed out across the pool of darkness to where the red light flickered before the tabernacle. Spell-bound, Mabel stayed where she was, poor Brother Leo listening to the outpourings of another St. Francis.

Other words of Reverend Mother Barat were engraved on her mind. She had spoken to the novices on the 21st of November, the fifty-eighth anniversary of her First Consecration in 1800, and had said of the Society, "It was founded on nothing as you can see, and God wanted it that way so that the souls called to be part of it should always consent to be nothing and to be looked on as the last of all. We have been despised and persecuted, but it must be so. I should no longer recognize our Society if it did not bear this resemblance to its Divine Master."

How Mother Barat loved, too, the poor and the little ones of this earth, urging her novices to love with an especial love those who stood in need of everything, warning them that only the grace of God constituted a title worthy of respect. There were her strong words, too, on love of the state of poverty that had been the choice of God the Son when He identified Himself with man. Two years were all too short to reach down to the depths of Reverend Mother Barat's simple teaching.

Cardinal Morlot, now Archbishop of Paris, insisted on performing the ceremony of First Vows. Mabel felt her heart could not contain all the joy that lay in her solemn promise before heaven and earth to serve God in the Society of His Sacred Heart by poverty, chastity and obedience. She re-read the words of Father Felix that she had written down while attending his retreat: "He is God, He is Man, He is Redeemer also, and with His Head crowned with thorns, His Heart pierced with sorrow, He says to us, 'See it is I, the Christ. Love me as I am.' Then our vocation can be thus expressed, like

Him to obey, to be humble, to sacrifice self always." There was her way straight before her. Three days after the Feast of the Annunciation she was journeying back to Marmoutier to take up work in the school. She did not know that the letter she carried to Mother Bosredont bore the testimony of a saint: "How full of promise is this new young religious of yours!"

There was bad news awaiting her from home. Kenelm after a brief illness had died in the spring, and Geraldine had made up her mind now that her duty lay with her mother. She wrote to Mabel that her father seemed to be softening. "If only they would send her to England," he had said of his nun daughter, "I should not mind, and we should meet again." But they had sent her to Marmoutier, and he was no religious to see in the orders of superiors the Will of God. There was nothing for his daughter to do but lay all her trust in God and to pray and work for the children entrusted to her care.

"We've got back our Novice," said Cécile. "She is Mistress of Discipline and I can tell you we keep her busy. But she keeps us in order, I can tell you also . . . and another thing, we like her all the time."

Chapter Twelve

1859—1864

THE late October gales had blown almost all the golden leaves from the trees as a horseman rode down through the woods beyond Caversham. There had been rain in the early morning, but the rent and ragged clouds had retreated and the sky was a calm faint blue. There were red haws in the hedges and spindleberries showed their orange hearts amid the tangle of old man's beard. The smell of good damp earth rose and the rich mouldering leaves carpeted the track. The road wound until it reached the river and the bridge across to Reading.

The rider reined in for a minute, watching the river flowing down to Windsor and Staines, miles away unseen beyond green meadows and wooded hills, through a countryside untouched by anything but the cycle of the seasons. The river was unchanged by the passing of a quarter of a century, yet on the far bank, shrill whistles and belching smoke showed where the railway lay close to the great gatehouse of the ruined abbey.

The horseman turned his mount across the bridge, and up toward the station. He dismounted stiffly and laboriously, and handed the reins to a loafer in the station yard. He took off his hat as though to let the breeze play through his graying hair and refresh his brow, then slowly made his way to the waiting-room. The ticket collector watched him curiously, then hastily called for help as he saw him collapse on a seat, and slide forward to the ground. The doctor was with him in a few minutes, but came too late. They searched his pockets for some clue to his identity. In a leather case they found what they looked for: papers bearing the name of Simon Digby.

Sister Digby had a full day before her. The school was waiting in its files for her, but Mother Bournonville came after her with a letter, smiling, and anticipating pleasure for her, since it came from England. Mabel took the letter and opened it. One glance and the words cut into her consciousness, bare and brutal in their manifest truth. Her father had gone from her with never a handclasp of reconciliation, no look into her eyes to say that the old intimacy had come back, safer now in their shared understanding of the full revelation of God, no assurance that his opposition to what she had done was no sin against the light. Only one thing was certain now: he was beyond her reach. Yes, but he was now in the realm where truth was unclouded, where human obstacles of upbringing, temperament and prejudice could no longer hide him from God's truth. Anything she could do for him now, he could receive. God had put straight into her hands this tremendous power of helping her father.

She slipped the letter into her pocket and gathered her books together. Even the daily duties of a teacher's life were linked to the Infinite and her fidelities, tiny, unnoticed, became a source of grace for him. Fighting back her tears, she turned to the school. She gave the signal with her wooden clapper and the work of the day began.

Her work was like that of her patron, St. Joseph, the watchful care of the Christ Child, who lived His Divine life in the souls of the children of the school. Unceasing, unwearying, kaleidoscopic, intensely human, intensely supernatural, it was work that left no excuse for selfishness, no unsatisfied longings for a fuller field of service.

At the end of one long day, Sister Digby had taken her place at the top end of the big study room. Before her stretched the rows of desks where the children were at the evening's task, pens newly sharpened scratching across the exercise books, heads bent over history books. Children, but immortal souls, souls in whom God dwelt. God . . . her thoughts lost themselves in His immensity, plunging into depth upon depth of His love. The clock chimed, striking her ear suddenly and loudly. With a start she came back to earth. Seven o'clock. What had she been doing in the last quarter of an hour, her duty forgotten, her very whereabouts ignored? What mischance had perhaps come upon her children? What account had she to give of her stewardship? Remorsefully, she asked pardon of Christ, "Dear Lord, surely Your children have done nothing to offend You while I neglected them." She raised her eyes to the study room's rows of desks. Beside each child stood a great winged being, strong, bright spirits watching the bent heads and busy hands. It seemed to her that a soft still voice spoke: "Not of set purpose was your distraction. See then, the Guardian Angels have kept these children from all evil."

Mother Gazelli replaced Mother Bosredont as superior. Her experienced eye saw in Mabel a good religious and a good teacher. She thought of her twenty-eight years, and then of her judgment and virtue. She weighed up her calmness, her tact, her spirit of conciliation, her firmness in the face of duty. She saw how within and without the convent she attracted people to her and won, unsought, their love. She took up her pen at last and wrote to Paris. Reverend Mother Barat smiled as she read the praise of "her little Digby."

"She knows already the spirit of the Sacred Heart . . . she is entirely docile . . . No one could second me better than she does . . . She knows each child individually . . . she influences them in a wonderful way. . . ."

It was obvious that Reverend Mother Gazelli wanted her as Mistress General. Obvious also that she would not ask it since it would mean losing so precious an aid for six months while she went through the training necessary before being professed. Reverend Mother Barat had summed up another side of Mabel's character. She could be asked for sacrifices and she would give them willingly for love of her Lord. She should continue to work in the school, and in the holidays she should come to the Mother House and join the other young nuns. Then, when the term began once more, she should return to Marmoutier, until the holidays again made her free to continue her probation. It would be hard to give up the happiness of uninterrupted contemplative life, but she already knew that hard things were precious. The old foundress understood her daughters. Like those first companions of hers who had braved revolutions and persecutions, poverty and hardships of all kinds, this one would have no need to be spurred on in the path of generosity and sacrifice. She, too, would run, would fly, would need, if anything, the curb.

For Mabel, they were wonderful days spent at the Mother House. Their obscurity was more dear to her than her position of authority in the interludes at Marmoutier. Too soon came the day when she was to make her final vows, to receive the ring and the cross that were the symbols of fidelity to a God who had given His all to her. The end had come to those blissful moments when the Mother General had beckoned her into her little room to talk together of God and of His goodness. Sitting in the circle with the other young nuns, on the eve of their dispersal, she watched the fire of love light up the old face as Reverend Mother Barat spoke to them with energy that belied her eighty-five years, and she thought with awe and reverence of the sixty-four years of selfless giving that had made it possible to hand on so great a treasure as the graces of the Sacred Heart into their unworthy keeping. She listened while anecdotes salted with Burgundian wit set them all laughing, then with a quick transition to seriousness, Reverend Mother Barat told them of an outbreak of yellow fever in America that had carried off seventeen of her nuns.

"Send us in their stead!" There was at once an eager chorus, but the foundress shook her head.

"Europe needs you, needs more and more of you." Yes, after Europe, America, Africa, Asia, Australia. There was no end to the asking. The whole world needed them, and yet she must send them to work first here in France. But the Lord of the harvest looked out on those other fields whitening for the laborers.

When the recreation was over, Reverend Mother Barat called Mabel to her. It might well be the last time. The sorrow that lay in Mabel's heart welled up.

"Reverend Mother, if only I knew, if only someone had been with my father at the end . . . some indication of his thoughts, his will. Was he turning against God's grace?"

There was a moment's silence. Then the quiet old voice spoke. "He is safe, my child."

The assurance of the tones filled Mabel with comfort. She looked up, still hesitant, finding a half smile on the face that looked down on hers. "We have been speaking of America. You will one day go to America. That will be God's answer to you, signifying the safety of your father's soul."

In the immediate future there was the work of Mistress General at Marmoutier. On the 7th of November, 1864, three days after making her Final Vows, Mabel said good-bye to the Mother House. She was never to see the foundress again. In the May of the following year she received a letter from her.

"Jesus will make up for all that you lack the very moment that you acknowledge that you do not lean on yourself, with all your own activity and plans, but ascribe all that you are and all that you do, to Our Lord. You will follow this practice with ease and delight if you understand the value and the necessity of the virtue of humility. Ah, if you become humble, the Heart of Jesus will do everything in you, and through you, in souls. Then you need fear nothing; your only spring of action will be the procuring of the glory of Jesus Christ, without fear or turning back upon yourself; but you must always remember that the means to employ should always be gentleness and charity."

It was the legacy of a saint. On May 25th Madeleine Sophie Barat died peacefully, and the burden of her work lay on younger shoulders.

To those who watched the young Mistress General at Marmoutier, it seemed as if the burden could not be too heavy. She did things with such ease and with such efficiency.

"How do you keep discipline so well?" asked Mother Zaepffel, struggling with her lively children.

"Pray to their guardian angels," Mother Digby answered. Was that all? Mother Zaepffel heard parents speaking of "a hand of iron in a velvet glove." Were you born with that kind of hand? She heard a priest say, "The spirit of wisdom is in her." She noted the strong, calm way Mother Digby cared for the children who were ill, the motherly love given to a small four-year-old, the fun and gaiety that broke out on holidays, the order and finish of all that she did. Guardian angels were no doubt given by God, but He gave also gifts to Mistress Generals. No wonder there was a special tenderness in Reverend Mother Gazelli's voice when she called her "my daughter."

Mother Zaepffel came upon Mother Gazelli and Mother Digby one early September day in 1865, as she turned a corner of the garden. They were seated under the great chestnut trees, while the autumn breeze checkered sunlight and shade. What was wrong? Down Mother Digby's face the tears poured silently. Startled, Mother Zaepffel cried out, "Reverend Mother, what is the matter with her?"

"She is going to replace me as superior," answered Mother Gazelli.

"Oh, if it's only that! It's not worth crying over," Mother Zaepffel exclaimed. Then some deeper understanding came to her. That still face bathed in tears was the face of one who was accepting suffering. That was the lot of a superior, her share of the cross of Christ, her ratification of the vow made when the cross of her profession was put around her neck. Mother Digby was starting on a new road to Calvary. "Very well, then," thought Mother Zaepffel, "you can count on me in life and in death. I want to be your Simon of Cyrene and help you to carry the cross God lays on you."

The sunshine through the trees was golden in spite of the shade.

III · All for His Glory
1866-1894

Chapter Thirteen

1866

MOTHER DIGBY glanced round the circle of her nuns
as they sat out in the garden for recreation one mild afternoon
of the holidays. They were her daughters, from the octo-
genarian hobbling on a stick to the recreation she could hear
no word of, to the twenty-year-old, rosy-cheeked, fresh from
the noviceship, eager to speak of St. John of the Cross and the
Canticle of Canticles. It had been a terrifying thought last
year to look at her large family and to know that she was the
youngest professed nun of them all, Superior before she was
thirty-one. She remembered the startled exclamation of the
Reverend Mother Vicar who had come to install her: "Good
gracious, how young she is!" Well, each year would rectify
that defect and there was the chance, too, that Paris would
discover its mistake and send someone else.

There were fresh arrivals from the noviceship whom she
could mother in all the stress of their new-fledged flights;
there were the old valiant warriors, past work or active still,
with their little oddities, like the gnarled bark of some ancient
sturdy oak, and their constant habit of prayer sending them
back to God as fish plunging into deep pools; there were the
middle-aged, working out their salvation in the rough and
smooth of life in common, and in the consolations and disap-
pointments attendant on the care of children. Yes, they were

all there, in the circle of nuns with their wicker baskets beside them, fingers moving with needle and thread, faces mirroring in so many different ways the Life that was the soul of their soul.

Now their superior was wondering, "When shall I tell them? The warning is not yet official. No need to spoil their rest with anxiety. Let them laugh away the time even if upstream the Loire is becoming swollen!" The chapel bell pealed. They all rose, gathered up their work, and went off to sing office. Golden September sunlight bathed the hills. The vines were ripening for the vintage. Droning bees, lazy last butterflies, the Newfoundland dog stretched out beside his kennel . . . and, beyond all this peace, the waters of the Loire gathering their forces.

She walked to the fields at the end of the property. They lay below the level of the river. In the meadow, the cows were peacefully moving from one green hillock to another. Gauthier the bailiff was standing by the beetroot field. He stooped down as she approached and pulled at the red leaves. The plant came out easily in his hand, and glancing down, she saw the water seeping into the empty hole. He nodded as the truth came to her.

"Yes, Reverend Mother, the floods are beginning. The river's not full yet, but . . ."

"How many days have we before the danger reaches us?"

He thought a minute. "We're at the 25th of September. They say the spate won't be till the 29th."

"Three full days. Well, Gauthier, we'll save a lot of the crops. You and the men, and I and the nuns, together we'll do something."

The first thing was to pray. She gathered the community and told them of the danger, infecting them with her high hopefulness.

"Pray with faith. I recommend two prayers: we shall ask Our Lady, O Mary conceived without sin, pray for us who have recourse to thee. And we shall say to the waters, Stop. The Heart of Jesus is with us." She made a chapel high up in the house. The Blessed Sacrament was there to watch over them. The nuns carried to the upper stories the chapel equipment. The food was put into safety. With her habit tucked up, Mother Digby was everywhere, helping, directing. The carpenter took off the heavy doors of the basement. The waters should move freely through the house. A new floor that had just been laid was taken up and plank by plank labelled. That should not suffer from warping. There was nothing left to spoil now on the ground floor.

Then they turned their attention to the gardens. Little ponds had begun to form beyond, nearer the river. The animals must first be brought into safety. Mother Digby headed the party that was to bring in the cattle. With feet splashing in unaccustomed cool pools, the cows eluded them, careering off with raised tails when the circle of nuns closed in on them. Precious time was lost, but at last they were on the move, through the open gate, up the path to the outhouses beyond possible reach of the flood waters.

The donkey was following the cows, but the tiny foal stood firm, legs apart, ears erect.

"Mother Zaepffel, bring him too."

More obstinate than a schoolchild, he sidled away from her approach, kicked up his heels, dug in his hoofs when she caught up with him, resisting all her tugging, then collapsed. She lifted him in her arms, triumphant, and turned to see the community gathered to applaud, and Mother Digby shaking with laughter.

The next day it was the turn of the fruit. In the orchards, the reddening apples were plucked from the branches, and the blue aprons of the nuns caught the sweet-smelling harvest. On the lower slopes of the hill, the grapes were ripening. Mother Digby took her band with tall wicker baskets and went up and down the rows of the vines, cutting the rich bunches hiding beneath the broad leaves, and piling high the vintage. At the end of the day, she climbed to the room in the old gate house that overlooked the highroad and the river. The sun was setting and throwing up the dark outline of the town in the distance across the Loire. Between Marmoutier and Tours ran the swollen river. Brown muddy waters swirled where a clear stream had meandered in the summer months, uprooted trees wallowed in the turgid waves, rafters and débris of houses were being carried down. The silent force of the river was gathering to a head.

"We still have tomorrow," said Mother Digby.

On the morrow they made their way down to the kitchen gardens and the fields planted with vegetables. The night had seen the trickles of water from the river grow in volume, and the soil was soaked.

"Tuck up your habits well," said Mother Digby, as they slithered across the mud of the beetroot field, and found their feet sinking deep into the squelching earth.

"The dyke has broken at Amboise," Gauthier told them. "It's giving way now at St. George's just by the city. They're saying you ought to go up the hill to Rougemont."

"Not yet," said Mother Digby, tugging at a carrot. "We can still save something. Mother Zaepffel, fetch the school bell. Gauthier, you will let me know at once if there is a breach near at hand. Then we will ring the bell, and immediately everyone must make for the house. In the meantime, we've work to do."

With laughter and jokes they cleared the vegetables from the ground, noting the ever-widening pools in the fields. The sky was sullen and overcast, but there was strength in the prayer Mother Digby sent up to the Sacred Heart of Jesus, Master of Wind and Water, and they were as light-hearted as the Newfoundland dog bounding among the baskets of carrots, as he laid down his own contribution carried from the field in his mouth.

As evening fell, Mother Digby sent the Community to bed, and took her Mother Treasurer with her out into the garden.

"How quiet it is!" she said, looking over to where lights were beginning to twinkle in Tours. "The sky seems to be brooding and waiting."

"There's no sound of bird song," said Mother Digby. "Even the grasshoppers are hushed. This is St. Michael's Day. He has always been our great protector. He will not fail us now."

They walked down toward the dyke when the sky darkened with the approach of midnight. The blackness of the country-side deepened when the flaming torches of the patrols flared along the river bank. Somewhere between them and the high hills watching like themselves in the distance beyond, ran the Loire, its swollen waters reaching their utmost height. There was no noise of shouting, no directions of man to man. There was no breeze stirring the trees, no lowing of cattle disturbed in their rest. The silence of waiting intensified, as from the distant church towers of Tours the chimes of midnight rang out. Suddenly a noise as of thunder rent the air. A great tearing and crashing of water drowned the excited shouts of men on the banks. The torches moved up and down, meeting and parting, wavering uncertainly. Gauthier ran up, panting.

"Reverend Mother, the banks have broken on the far side. The overflow of waters is pouring out into the fields beyond. We're saved!"

The next morning, when they had offered their thanks to God at Mass, Mother Digby led the nuns to the top of the old tower. They looked across to where the river had once flowed through its raised banks. A great stretch of water, sparkling like an inland lake under the bright September sun, lay before them, covering familiar fields and farmlands.

"The Loire and the Cher have met and mingled their

waters," said Mother Digby, letting her gaze wander over the wild waste of flood. Truly God had had her nuns in His keeping. There was damage to their property, but not irreparable. This time they were safe. Next time . . . there must not be a next time when they would be in danger in the old house. There was but one thing to be done. She must build a safer refuge for her family. While they were watching and exclaiming, her mind was already pressing forward with possibilities. Yes, she must build.

Chapter Fourteen

1867

MOTHER DIGBY mounted the ladder, looking upward to the blue sky cross-laced with the scaffolding. At the third story, she swung herself on to the planks that ran along by the unfinished wall, where the men had left trowels and mortar, empty hods and piles of bricks. They were under the trees, with bread and cheese and bottles of wine, waiting for the apples she had sent Sister Beaucé to bring them for their midday meal. She smiled as she remembered the Sister's remark: "When I'm old, Reverend Mother, I shall boast of the time I mounted the scaffold with you." She was alone this time. Mother Vercruysse, her Assistant, seemed to have been delayed. If she was not to be late for Community recreation, she must make her round of inspection by herself.

The new building was going up quickly. When they had dug

the foundations, the workmen had come upon the graves of long-forgotten monks beneath the smooth green grass . . . forgotten, but they had played their part in handing on the faith. The abbey they had raised to house the Incarnate God had been pulled down till only a few stones remained on stones, but He still dwelt in the place. Timelessly, through the green fields beyond the house she was raising, the Loire flowed on as it had in the days when St. Gatien and St. Martin looked out on it; as it would flow in the centuries to come when someone stood in her place and watched the rising of a new building.

She moved along, noting the beams crossing from wall to wall to support the floor. The men were working well. She stepped out on a crossbeam with steady feet and cool head as she had done many a time before over the empty space between. Then without warning the plank beneath her slipped sideways and down. She felt herself thrown outward. The scaffolding reeled around her and she dropped between the joists, her hand clutching desperately at the poles. With a jerk the downrush ended. She swung there for age-long seconds between heaven and earth, while her fingers stiffened with the strain. Then two hands closed over hers. She was aware of Mother Vercruysse's white face above, of laughter from the nuns below as they came out to recreation, of blue sky and the beating against it of black-winged birds, of a dog barking, of undisturbed green fields and a river that flowed on, and then she was standing again on the plank, white and breathless, with Mother Vercruysse beside her.

"Get right back to the wall," said the Mother Assistant, wondering still how without the help of the Guardian Angels she could have dragged her superior up again to safety.

Mother Digby closed her eyes. There were deep wells of space between her and the wall and only threads of beams to walk upon. The scaffolding wheeled kalcidoscopically. Her feet seemed rooted to the plank. Across the open gulf of the buildings stood the firm wall and broader plank-covered passage. She opened her eyes resolutely. She must get across the abyss. Mother Vercruysse could not help her on that narrow ledge of beam. She could not walk across. Very well, then she would run. Looking neither to left nor right, she moved swiftly over. She felt her hands at last against the rough mortar of the wall. She forced herself to look downward. The workmen were still lounging beneath the trees. Sister Beaucé was only just emerging from the kitchen with her basket of apples. Mother Digby turned and smiled at Mother Vercruysse. "We shall be late for recreation," she said, and when they reached the bottom of the ladder, she added, "Not a word of this to anyone."

Gauthier came to her one day. "I'd like you to come along, Reverend Mother, and have a look. You know that old cherry tree that doesn't bear any more fruit. We were digging it up to burn it—it's got roots that go down a mighty long way—suddenly the earth's all caved in and there's a great hole underneath."

She went along with him. The uprooted tree lay unregarded beside a large cavity. She stepped down into it, and saw before her a passage stretching out into the darkness. "We must explore this properly," she said.

"They do say the old monks had a treasure hidden away," Gauthier remarked hopefully.

At midday Mother Digby arrived with a band of nuns with candles and hurricane lanterns. Down into the dark passage they climbed, stumbling over blocks of stone embedded in the damp soil of the floor, their shadows running up and down the vaulted walls. Then the way widened out and their upturned lanterns showed them a great underground quarry, the tool marks of long dead masons still fresh on the walls. Bent double, they peered into arched excavations where huge blocks of stone had been cut and piled, awaiting their removal to their place in some new building. The dust of centuries lay upon them. Mother Digby moved on. The light of her lantern was reflected suddenly beyond in a black pool. The nuns thinned out to a single file, skirting the still waters whose cool silence seemed to rise in protest against their echoing feet. At the end, a shaft rose up and showed the sky distantly.

"Why, this must be the spring of St. Gatien's Well!" cried Mother Zaepffel. It was strange to wander here as though in another world, a world of the past, alive yet not alive, dead yet speaking with living tones.

"We have stumbled on the clue to the old grottoes of the monks and saints," said Mother Digby. "Somewhere here we shall find the shrines perhaps of those early Christians who first said Mass in Marmoutier."

Above them the sun shone and children played, here they were near in the gloom to those whose work lived on. As they retraced their footsteps and came out into the hot, bright afternoon, it was as though they had traversed eighteen centuries and had communed with Gatien, the man who had heard among the Seventy-two disciples the voice of Christ saying, "Pray the Lord of the Harvest that He sends laborers into the harvest . . . Go . . . behold I send you," and who had in his turn, when he had laid his bones in the soil of France, repeated to them this charge. The past was very near.

Eva was waiting for her when Mother Digby returned to the house. She had come down the hill from Rougemont, where she had been spending some of the summer months with her mother, to say good-bye before going back to England.

"It's been lovely here, Mabel," she said, her eyes sparkling. "Lovely to see you, and the Mothers and Sisters I knew at school. School was beginning to feel a long way off. I'm getting old."

"Twenty-four," commented her sister, laughing. "What are you doing with life?"

"I don't know. God wants me somehow . . . but I couldn't be a nun. Perhaps I'll get married. Mama and Geraldine think I am frivolous sometimes. I love life so much, Mabel."

The sunlight was on her rosy face. "Anyhow, there's time still before me."

She chattered inconsequently, followed her sister into the house, made her round of happy good-byes, and last of all greeted Mabel. As she went through the door, she turned quickly, ran back and put her arms about her sister with sudden intensity.

"Mabel, this is the last time I shall see you on earth."

There was a quick swing-to of a door. Eva was out in the sunshine of the path, her golden hair haloing her face. The dankness of the grottoes seemed to fill the house.

The archaeologists of Tours lent a hand in the exploration. An old plan of the Abbey showed where the chief shrines had been. But men had joined hands with time and the tombs were empty, and broken statuary marked the path of early pillagers. The picks of the excavators opened other grottoes around the central sanctuary. In some slept skeletons with folded arms as when they were first laid there, in others only a little heap of bones was left. No record, no name was there to say who they were. Bare humanity witnessed to its end. But from the skull of one a great root stretched upward, burying itself in the soil between the fissured rock and giving life to a sapling larch green in the midst of the autumnal trees.

The new building was already in use in the spring of 1868. The happy shouting and laughter of the children filled its rooms. A new generation was beginning to make of it a dwelling place where their thoughts would home in the years to come. Only from England came disquieting news. The cold and damps of winter had left Eva with a cough she could not shake off.

The archbishop arrived from Tours to see the work of restoration of the grottoes.

"We have no money for more, Your Grace," said Mother Digby. "We were thinking of closing the tombs again."

"Yes," he answered her. "Let them sleep in peace. Time has respected them. It is so well with them, why should we disturb them?"

That June Mrs. Digby wrote to say that Eva had received Extreme Unction. The doctors held out little hope. She was wasting away, clinging fiercely to life with all the desire of twenty-five years, but losing the battle step by step. Yet in the peace of the Last Sacraments she had seen what it was that God asked of her. She was to be as wholly His as her sister the nun. She would offer her life for the supernatural life of her brother Essex. To Marmoutier she sent a last letter.

My Darling Sister Mabel,

How glad I am to feel you pray so much for your little sister! Oh, how happy I am! I feel nearer to God than I ever did, and can lie for hours thinking of Him and of glorious heaven. But may be I shall suffer yet more, and I should so wish to please our dear Lord by bearing all patiently. . . . Oh, dear Mabel, what a sacrifice not to see you again! I love you so! We shall meet again in our home up above. I throw myself on the mercy of God; how I long to see Him! I can write no more. Adieu.

Your loving sister, Evy.

On January 28th, 1869, Eva died. The sapling larch whose root stretched down to the skull of a forgotten monk was covered at the time with snow, like a cherry tree in blossom.

The grottoes were shut again. Their legendary wealth was not brought to light. The old monks had their treasure hidden away. Gauthier knew part of its secret as in the bleak March weather he planted the seeds for the crops of the distant summer. Two seasons were to fulfill their cycles before Essex and his young wife were received into the Church.

Chapter Fifteen

1870—1871

MOTHER DIGBY stood by the window overlooking the high road. The stream of refugees had been passing all day, old men and women, sturdy peasant women with bundles, children dragging tired feet, as they clung to the sides of perambulators piled high with poor family possessions, or trailed in the wake of handcarts pushed by weary men. It was heartbreaking to see them, driven by fear from the invaded provinces to the north, infecting all Touraine with their alarm. From the green fields of the convent rose unceasing the plaintive baaing of a great flock of sheep. She had opened the gates to them and their footsore shepherds the day before. Thirteen days on the march had thinned the animals and they huddled together with wide, scared eyes. What more were the men and women moving away from the clash of armies than sheep wandering pathetically, grateful for any green grass that life could offer them, if but for a few hours? What could she do to soften pain?

The peasants from the neighborhood had come with their treasures for her to keep in safety: the fierce old goat tethered in the meadow was old Juliette's pride, the brindled cow in her herd belonged to the Menthon family; she had stores of household linen in safety in her cupboards . . . but these were only token kindnesses. The stream of suffering still ran by. There were some of her own daughters weeping for brothers dead on battlefields, where gallantry and high heroism were the only fruits of combat. For them she had a mother's tender sympathy. Her doors had opened to some fifty nuns driven out by the German advance, from other houses of the Society. They had to be made to forget—by full adherence to the Will of God— the destruction of their work.

There were the day-to-day anxieties of not knowing what was happening elsewhere, of hearing rumors of the horrors of the siege of Paris by the German army, where Reverend Mother Lehon and her small community filled the great empty buildings of the Mother House, of having no communication with the Mother General, forced to take refuge in Laval. Then, with only a dozen children in the boarding school, it was difficult to maintain over eighty nuns. Poverty was real, causing her to work like the poorest for bare subsistence. But in their poverty, there was spiritual joy and humility, and here in Marmoutier reigned the spirit of Christ, their Lord and Model. Outside, conflicts and sufferings, wars and tyrannies were the fruit of the desire for riches. If a breath of the spirit of poverty could be sent out from their walls throughout the world, strife would cease, passions would be calmed, and happiness would take the place of the anxiety and sadness that wore out so many lives. It was being forced on them all now; she prayed that they might taste the joy of those who give what was in reality nothing, to gain what was all.

A knock at the door. Her Mother Assistant, Mother Filling, was there.

"Reverend Mother, I do not know if you have heard. They say that the Republican Government at Tours has ordered the expulsion of all Germans from France. What will you do with me and your other German daughters?"

Mother Digby picked up a letter from the table. "Don't

worry, Mother. Monsieur Gambetta and his fellow ministers are living at Archbishop's House. The Cardinal writes that we have no need to fear. The Republic is his guest, and he will see to it that it does not touch any of his nuns."

Mother Filling still lingered. "Reverend Mother, there is an old couple waiting in the parlor for you, the Rollins from the cottage next to St. Radegonde's. They say they must see you."

"I will come at once."

They were sitting on the edge of their chairs, with a large parcel on the parlor table between them. Their faces looked pinched and anxious, but an answering smile came when Mother Digby greeted them.

"Well, Mathilde, what can I do for you?"

The old woman pushed the parcel toward her. "It's like this, Reverend Mother. They say the Germans are advancing, that they'll arrive here in Tours soon. There's my sister's child down Bordeaux way . . . she wants us to go to her. We'll have to leave the cottage. We'll not be able to take things with us . . . they say the soldiers are terrible, smashing and stealing. We're not wealthy, Reverend Mother, and there's not much they can spoil in our place, nothing they can take away except these. But we couldn't have them destroy these . . . they're all the treasure we've got."

Her trembling gnarled fingers were fumbling with the knots of the parcel. Mother Digby waited, then unfolded the paper when the string was loose. There came the sweet smell of lavender, and she saw before her a white veil, yellowing with age, the neatly folded bridal dress, the bridegroom's coat and trousers and neckerchief.

"Our wedding dresses . . . we wouldn't want to lose them after fifty years together. Would you mind them for us, Reverend Mother?"

Mother Digby folded the paper carefully round them. Of course she would keep them safe. All their treasure, the treas-

102

ure of poor people. God had given to her and to each of her nuns a wedding garment. What did it matter if they were poor? That treasure was theirs.

She went on to the community room for the morning's work. They were all hard at the task, great piles of canvas billowing out over the floor. She took her place and picked up an end of material. An old nun, with fingers too weak to manage the coarse stuff, handed her a threaded needle and watched for the next stitcher who should need one.

"Reverend Mother, this is the seven hundred and nineteenth tent we've made," cried out a young sister, folding up the finished canvas.

"We'll change our occupation this afternoon," said Mother Digby. "The cows are running short of fodder. We'll go along to the vine terraces and gather the vine leaves. Then we shall be sure they will not starve."

She had made provision for her daughters already. Crops, fruit and grapes were all stored safely. There would be enough to help any wounded soldiers they should be sent. She had already transformed the old buildings into a hospital for them. Former classrooms furnished with clean white beds made bright wards, and in the midst she had furnished a chapel in the largest, where Christ Himself should watch over them. October was ending in gloom. It seemed only too true that Bazaine had capitulated without defending Lorraine, and that now the Prussian armies could swing down toward the hastily raised, ill-equipped army of the Loire.

On November 1st, Mother Digby encouraged the nuns at midday recreation. All the saints of God rejoicing in heaven ... that was the real truth of life, a fact of faith that left always the possibility of happiness. As she spoke, a dull rumbling sound broke in on them across the countryside, distant but unmistakable. It was the noise of gunfire. They listened.

"It is in the direction of Orleans," said Reverend Mother Digby. "The armies have met. Pray, pray for all those who fight."

The next day the convent doctor called. "Reverend Mother, my son is being put in charge of your hospital. We shall send you serious surgical cases. We are quite satisfied with your arrangements. We shall send you the first cases tonight."

Dr. Herpin looked at her. He admired the calm of this Englishwoman. He would not mince matters with her. "Things are going badly, Reverend Mother. There has been fierce fighting around Orleans. Perhaps the Maid has put courage into our Frenchmen. But courage needs something more if it is to stand up to the steel cannons from Krupp's. We've lost the town. It looks to me as if Gambetta does not think well of the safety of Tours. He is leaving for Bordeaux. You will not have a sinecure here."

Mother Digby smiled at him. "Thank you, Dr. Herpin. We have put the keys of this house into St. Martin's care. He will see us through."

"Take care of your own health," he said. He knew how little her daughters were aware of her headaches and physical weakness.

She laughed at him, shrugging off his fears. How could she tell him that in her love of her Lord she had asked Him never to leave her without some pain? His wisdom would temper it so that her work for others would not suffer. And, anyhow, what were the little aches in comparison with the pain of the wounded who were carried into the house that night?

Chapter Sixteen

1870—1871

" "M A D A M E the Surgeon-in-Chief!" remarked the surgeon, wiping his fingers on the towel and watching the short white-overalled nun disappear through the door. "Where did she learn it all? I'd much rather have her help me than many a trained doctor. Did you notice during that amputation how she anticipated what I wanted and how steady her hands were all the time? Who taught her?"

"Natural gift, some of it," said Herpin, getting into his coat. "The rest she's got looking after the sick nuns and the children here. No nonsense with her. You should see the way she sends the girls packing if they try being 'interesting' with her, and yet when there's anything really wrong she's tenderness itself."

"These soldiers are like children to her," commented the surgeon. "She gives them confidence. There's strength in her pity."

"She's a valiant woman herself. A year or two back, one of the nuns was dying. The only hope was to cauterize her throat . . . you know, apply a metal disc about the size of louis d'or. She couldn't face it. Reverend Mother pulled up her sleeve, took the red-hot disc, and put it on her own arm without flinching. And somehow that heartened the other nun and she let me get on with her throat. Yes, and she recovered."

"Well, doctor, if you can get her for me whenever there's an operation to be done, I'll thank you. I think we shall have to take off Bernard Perez' leg . . . I don't imagine we shall save his life otherwise. What's the noise?"

Dr. Herpin smiled. "Oh, only the men saying their night prayers. Your Surgeon-in-Chief is also Bishop *in partibus* . . . only she's living in the midst of the pagans of her diocese. She's working wonders, she and the chaplain and the rest of the community. St. Martin will begin to recognize the Eldest Daughter of the Church again if this goes on much longer."

The surgeon grunted. It was strange to find so intelligent a man as good Dr. Herpin believing in medieval superstitions still. However, undoubtedly the atmosphere of happiness in this hospital was getting the patients on their feet again very quickly.

Mother Digby was tired. In a few hours the caller would be at her door and the long day would begin over again. But sleep was God's gift to His beloved, and He gave strength for the work in hand. Within the Convent all was hushed. Outside under the sharp frost the countryside was still. Her eyes closed in the quiet darkness.

The clanging of the alarm bell broke the peace. Rising hastily, she went down to the enclosure door. The guard of the hospital stood there, shuffling his hobnailed boots uncomfortably. At the sight of Mother Digby, relief brought the words tumbling out.

"Reverend Mother, if you please, sorry to trouble you, we couldn't do anything with him, it's the man René, whose calf has been shot away, he says you can fix it for him, the bandages, we can't get at him, he keeps asking for you."

"I'll come at once."

She followed the guard down the dark corridors and into the ward. She trimmed one of the shaded lamps and brought it

106

across to the bed. Setting it down, she folded back the bed
clothes, and began work on the bandages. René was uttering
little moans of pain, but under her gentle fingers he grew quiet.

"Very sorry, Reverend Mother, very sorry to disturb you,
but only you can fix my leg properly."

She smiled, smoothing out the bedclothes, and shaking up
the pillow. "Is that all right, now?"

He nodded gratefully. No wonder his little son had wanted
Mother Digby in the first place in heaven next to Mother Barat.

In the shadows of the bed next to René, two fever-bright
eyes were watching the nun busy about her task, noting her
kind gestures and the motherly softness of her gaze. Looking up from her task, Mother Digby saw him. She knew the
poor lad. His leg had been amputated some weeks ago, but he
made no improvement, speaking little, lying with his face
from the rest of the ward, taciturn, unhappy, with a barrier
raised around his unhappiness. She rose, lifted the lamp, went
over to him, and said quietly, "Can I do something for you?"
He shook his head, his eyes on her still. She turned down the
lamp, and moved away, aware that his gaze was following her
all the way, and at the door she suddenly knew that she was
for the first time on the other side of the barrier he had raised.

There was a cold wind cutting under doors and along the
dark corridors. The frost was striking in through the bleak
stone walls. She thought, "We must go out tomorrow to the
woods and gather more broken branches." The wounded were
coming in half frozen. Strange that even the weather seemed
to have aligned itself with the enemies of France. Holy Father
Olivaint, when she had last met him in Paris, had spoken of the
evil that was in all the life of France, sapping its vigor by
unbelief and immorality. He had welcomed suffering as Our
Lord had welcomed it, as the road to redemption. Bitter frosts
or exploding shells, they both led to the threshold of eternity.

He had said, "Your sufferings will serve like His to draw down pardon on others. If we saw things in the light of God, it would be impossible for us to be afraid, for the worst would be the best." She must remember this, and accept her little measure with gratitude.

The next day as she went around doing dressings in the wards, Bernard Perez called her.

"Reverend Mother, here's this fool of a surgeon saying that my leg must come off. I'm rather attached to it, you know. Can you do anything about it?"

She raised her eyebrows, knowing her man. "It's that, or your life."

"All the same, Reverend Mother . . . if you pleaded with the doctors for me?"

"They've told you the truth. If you want me to plead with anyone, it must be God."

He pulled a wry face. "You're as bad as our good friend the chaplain. He's been arguing fit to talk a donkey's hind leg off to convince me that there's another life after this, in which it would be better I should hobble around on one leg the fewer . . . but this donkey's only got two legs and I am not convinced by his talking. You must keep me alive, Reverend Mother, leg and all, and I shall write a special article about you in my newspaper when this war's over."

"You will only keep alive with your two legs if you pray. Come, now, I will see the surgeon today; you must let me dress your leg without making a fuss, and if you won't pray yourself, at least be ready to acknowledge that our prayers have value if we manage to save you altogether."

She moved on. René was comfortably asleep. The boy next to him was wide-eyed for her approach. He fumbled under his pillow and brought out a small box and a letter. He looked at her in silence. She helped him with a quiet "What is it?"

"It's . . . I've got a girl . . . we were going to get married after the war. I've written to her; here's the letter. I've put in the box the little bits of bone they took from my leg. I'll not get better . . . will you send it all to her . . . after?"

She took it very gently from him.

"I will write a letter to her myself and tell her everything. Do you want anything else?"

"No . . . yes . . . a crucifix, Reverend Mother."

She gave him one, and he kissed it reverently. The tears were rolling down his cheeks, but his face had lost its hard look. She would send the priest to him to help him in his last fight. It would not be far distant now.

The days of December were icy. A cold wind swept the land and there were early falls of hard-frozen snow. In Paris, dog cutlet and *ragoût* of rat were delicacies. Reverend Mother Digby looked at the hens clucking around in the barnyard and decided that she would not take the advice of those who feared they would be stolen by the invading armies. The eggs were needed for her patients. St. Martin must keep them safe. She would not have them killed.

On the morning of December 20th, the roll of gunfire sounded near. The children ran to her, terrified and excited. She calmed them by her imperturbable quiet, remembering young colts brought up against a sudden noise. She set them to work in the ordinary routine of their day, then walked with a group of nuns up the hillside to Rougemont. The cold cut through their shawls, reddening their hands and pinching their fingers. The earthy ruts, frozen hard, crumbled beneath their feet, dead leaves bore a silver edging of frost. Below them the fields began to dwindle to squares of black furrows lined with the unmelted snow, or patches of white pasture-land where cows huddled in corners. The trees stood up black and the river ran like a steel ribbon across the scene. As they paused a moment in their ascent, Mother Filling said, "The earth is the Lord's and the fullness thereof, the world and all they that dwell therein."

Mother Digby nodded, gazing at the symphony of black and white. "All these beauties are ours, for the instruction and full development of our powers."

"Why don't people see that?" Mother Vercruysse queried.

"Only the pure of heart can see God in creation," said Mother Digby, and added "and only the humble of spirit and tender of heart discern the hand of God in the working out of human affairs. Only humility has the insight to discover it, the depth to follow it up to its conclusions and the breadth to love it, wheresoever it may be found. I think that to humility is granted discernment and insight."

They had reached the top at last and from the house looked down on the little town of Monnaye. The cannons' roar was loud, and the smoke of battle rose all about. Mother Digby stood between Mother Filling and Mother Vercruysse, French, English and German so united in their common hopes and desires. It seemed cruel folly that, beneath them, men of different nations should be killing each other.

They went into the building and began to pack together some of the movable furniture. Suddenly, the noise of firing ceased, and the silence rose menacing from the land beneath them. Carrying some of their packages, they went down the hill again and saw the lights begin to shine out in the windows of Marmoutier. But before darkness enwrapped the old monastery, they saw men marching down the roads to east and west encircling them. They marched in good order, perfectly disciplined. Along the high road by the Loire, where once St. Joan had ridden on her white horse, the gray guns of the Prussian army passed by relentlessly.

In the morning, from the hillsides all around them, the German guns opened fire on Tours. Mother Digby listened to the long whistling whine as the shells passed over, and learned to time the sound of their noisy explosion. Then the bombardment ceased and Gauthier reported that the mayor was parleying with the invaders. While they spoke, Reverend Mother Digby was acting. Through falling snow, she led the way up again to Rougemont. Over the slippery freezing ground, they carried down to Marmoutier all the furniture and fittings of the old house. Those things at least should be saved from destruction.

"What about these old desks?" asked Mother Vercruysse. "The children don't use them now."

"Leave them," said Mother Digby, looking round the empty rooms and wondering who would be their next inhabitants. When they were back again in Marmoutier, she found wounded Prussians being brought to her hospital. She welcomed them and made them as comfortable as she could. It was the eve of Christmas, when the Son of God had looked for shelter.

Chapter Seventeen

1871

O N January 28th, after one hundred and thirty days of siege, Paris capitulated. Fifteen thousand of the occupying German forces were quartered in Touraine and the old desks left at Rougemont were the mangers for forty German horses. The Red Cross flag over the old abbey buildings protected French and Germans alike, and the nuns were left in peace. But with an army to feed, the countryside grew short of food.

Stephen, the old farm laborer, pushed the convent handcart through the gatehouse door and made his way down to Tours. Reverend Mother had told him to get some food. An hour later, he was back again. Mother Digby looked at his empty cart.

"Well, Stephen?"

He pushed back his cap and scratched his head. "Well, Reverend Mother, I got to the bridge. There are great cannons posted all the way along. I found myself looking bang down the nozzle of one of them and the Prussians standing by. Stephen, I says to myself, I'm thinking it's not the Reverend Mother's intention that you should be killed. If the Emperor and the King of Prussia have any difference of opinion between 'em, let 'em settle it themselves. Why do they want to make war on the likes of us?"

Why, indeed? Yet war generated special graces and manly virtues. God Himself had said He came to bring war . . . In His war there could be no question of truce or diplomatic settlement.

"We must remain armed," she thought. "There are times when the world will offer us an olive branch of peace. Nature is willing to acquiesce and the devil is there to encourage our sloth. We must remember that we have no abiding city here below . . . when we are in an enemy country we must look to our defenses and ask ourselves if our fidelity is proof against temptation, so that we may stir up in others and in ourselves the courage and trust which are pledges of victory. I wish we all had the spirit that rejoices in this kind of conflict and ignores discouragement and frustration. Poor Stephen, I shall have to try to put some spirit into him, too."

She sent him out again next day. A large painted red cross decorated his cart. A hundred yards down the road he ran into a squad of Prussians. They seized his cart and went off with it. Stephen watched it disappearing without protest. They would not have understood French in any case, he considered philosophically. Mother Filling was not so philosophical.

"Yes, Reverend Mother," she said to Mother Digby, "I will certainly write in your name to the commanding officer. They must return our property."

"Ask for a pass, also, for Stephen. We must feed our invalids."

Mother Filling's letter was delivered. The cart was returned, the pass obtained. Hungry mouths could now be satisfied, so long as provisions were obtainable. Mother Filling was grateful that her countrymen stood well in the eyes of her superior. Elsewhere they met with so much hatred.

The first comers to the hospital were getting on well. René's calf had healed. Bernard Perez' leg, against all expectation, was still his own. Only two men had died. There were quite a number able to hobble about now. Mother Digby was going her rounds, dressing the wounds of those still in bed, smiling at the jokes of the convalescents lounging in chairs or walking the corridors. Suddenly a soldier by the window gave a shrill whistle. She turned hastily, catching sight of a trousered leg disappearing into the bed next to her. Not a man was to be seen in chairs or corridors. Each bed showed the humped form of a sick man with languid head upon the pillow, and bedclothes well pulled up about his neck. Perez beside her chuckled.

"Good combined operations, Reverend Mother. Don't give us away. The boys are mortally afraid of being sent as prisoners to Germany. We keep a look-out for Prussian officers. There's a group of them just come in now. We're so ill we couldn't put a foot to the floor. Isn't that right, Reverend Mother?"

There was one empty bed. "Where's René?" Mother Digby asked.

Perez closed one eye. "My leg's dreadfully painful, Reverend Mother. Could you carry on with the dressings?"

The military visitors asked her to take them around. They noted the orderliness of all the arrangements, the sleeping men, the comforts provided.

"Madame, we shall send you more cases when you have empty beds," said the officer in command. "I trust you will keep us informed when such vacancies occur."

Behind his back Perez opened one eye. Reverend Mother was leading the Prussians past René's bed, engaging them in conversation. She was through the door with them. The sentry by the window reported they were going out on to the path, were through the gateway, were out on to the high road. Mother Digby returned. Chairs and corridors were filling again with men. René was still not to be seen.

"Haven't you a cistern upstairs?" Perez queried innocently. She mounted to the loft. In the dusk she saw two eyes watching her from the shelter of the overarching beams.

"René, what are you doing?"

"Reverend Mother, as a franc-tireur is not so popular with the German authorities, I was going to get into the cistern if they had searched the house."

She sent him downstairs, sighing to herself. These men were children, good or naughty, but still children, needing a mother. Willingly she would spend herself and be spent for them. It was a grief to see that whereas the Prussian soldiers had each a prayer book in their haversacks the Frenchmen for the most part had nothing and knew nothing. She would in her prayers be in labor until Christ should be brought forth in them. In the meantime, she would fill their pockets with apples and send them out into the sunshine to play skittles in the newly-made alley down by the enclosure wall.

The days were lengthening toward spring. More and more convalescents sunned themselves in the field and laughed over the game. German sentries along the road crept nearer and nearer to the wall. On the raised levée, they watched enviously. René, pockets bulging with fruit as in those happy distant days when Reverend Mother Barat looked out of windows at her "young gentlemen" and legalized orchard marauding, tossed up an apple to them. The others lobbed up more in their turn, applauding catches and deriding misses. Back to them came a shower of cigarettes. Emperors were forgotten as teeth met in juicy fruit and thin whiffs of smoke rose in the air.

In March dire news arrived from Paris. Everywhere in the streets the barricades were up, houses, churches and shops were blazing as the Communards fired them with petroleum. Hostages had been seized and crowded into the prisons, and the Revolutionary forces had the capital in their power. The Red Flag was appearing in other towns, perhaps Tours would in its turn be taken. April came and Frenchman slaughtered Frenchman while the Prussian occupying forces looked on. Blue skies and the opening leaves of May spoke ironically of returning life while the Archbishop of Paris, Father Olivaint and hundreds of other hostages were shot in cold blood. In Marmoutier, the school children had returned to their classes, and school life was re-establishing itself with all the carefree interests of growing children, while Mother Digby and her nuns waited anxiously for any details of the fate of their Sisters in the Mother House. Not till the opening weeks of June could their fears be allayed, and the full work of the Society take its course in the midst of hatred and destruction.

The last beds were empty in the hospital. The last soldiers stood at the gate waiting to say good-bye to the Mother Superior. There were smiles on their faces as they pushed one of their number forward to speak their thanks, but there was still a little sadness that the happy days in the old Monastery were at an end. She shook their hands, guessing what their tongues could not express. They turned and filed out. The spokesman hesitated, feeling that all had not been said. Then very earnestly, gripping her hand hard, he cried in parting:

"I wish you, Reverend Mother, plenty of promotion!"

Then he was off up the road and the sound of their marching feet died away.

Chapter Eighteen

1872

O N August 4th, 1872, the carriage belonging to the convent stood ready waiting in the outer courtyard. The clock struck ten. Quickly Mother Digby came out with a companion and stepped in. The Mother Assistant closed the door, the horse moved forward and they passed under the gateway and out on to the road. There was to be no fuss or expressed regrets when the Will of God asked for a sacrifice. She knew the community within would hear the rolling of the wheels, the clip-clop of the hoofs on the hard, dusty road, but she knew that they would be glad to be trusted to offer their human pain joyfully to God's all-loving providence. She knew that even now they would be gathered round the notice she had pinned up for them, and accepting her last message. She so longed for them to give their very best to Him who had given His best to them. Hard to sum all that up in a few words. She had written finally, "May the love of the Heart of Jesus, zeal for His glory, a longing for His Will be yours all through time and in eternity."

Behind her the walls of Marmoutier were growing smaller, guardian of so many lovely things, lovelier because of the price she had often paid for them, pain and joy running together in the present realization of their worthwhileness. She could not spoil them with a backward glance.

The train carried her to Paris, setting the long miles between her and the beloved house and the daughters she was handing over to another's care. At the station the Mother House carriage awaited her and she drove through the streets that still bore in their ruins the fiery traces of the Commune. Gone were the Tuileries, the Palais de Justice and the Hôtel de Ville. The Republic was bringing about a different Paris, a changing France. On the hill of Montmartre, the faith of the country saw one day a great basilica to the Sacred Heart where France could make reparation for her sins and those of the world. Just beyond the walls of the city, where the Seine and Marne mingled their waters, lay the body of Mother Barat, bequeathing that duty of loving reparation to her daughters. She could hear her words echoing in her heart: "If we loved, our motto would be Work, Love and Suffer."

"Reverend Mother Lehon will go with you and install you," said Mother Goetz. Mother Lehon, the intrepid, going on quietly with her dinner in the Mother House refectory when a German shell had exploded in the story above, arguing with a drunken soldier while he held his musket to her breast, calmly removing money and incriminating papers from under the noses of the Communards who had forced their way into the house. But the English Reverend Mother had courage, too, though she would need it in a different way. England across the moating Channel looked peaceful. There seemed little chance of persecution of the kind that had made the glory of her martyrs. But there were other battles to be fought there.

Looking down on Mother Digby kneeling beside her, the Mother General saw how her humble novice of old had plunged into a deeper humility. Yes, she would be equal to the task before her, equal to winning the love of the community at Roehampton, who were grieving for the departure of a dearly loved superior, equal to gaining the hearts of English children, and to moving forward in any work that the Holy Spirit should make clear to her. There was, too, a humorous attitude these Englishwomen had toward difficulties and dangers. It was the same with Henrietta Kerr, who would be making her final profession in a few days' time. Her laughter and fun had carried her and her companions through the difficult days in Rome two years ago, when the rabble that had invaded the Holy City and made Pius IX a prisoner in the Vatican had threatened the existence of the nuns in the Trinità. And at recreations Mother Digby's laughter welled up in just the same spontaneous way. Yes, it betokened courage.

To Mother Digby it seemed strange to be returning to England after fifteen years. Eva, Kenelm, her father . . . they would not be there in reality as they were in memory. They belonged to a changeless world untouched by time, but the land she was to live in now was different from the one she remembered. On the 17th of August, with Reverend Mother Lehon, she took the train to Calais and boarded the steamer for England.

At Barnes the two Reverend Mothers found a carriage waiting to take them up Roehampton Lane. They left behind them the gorse-covered common and rode between dusty banks crowned with hawthorn with reddening berries and seeded cow-parsley. Tall elms rose in an avenue before them. Reverend Mother Lehon glanced at her young companion seated silent and still beside her. She had the air of a condemned prisoner awaiting execution. The man checked the horse and turned through a green gate. The warm evening sun glinted on a tiny sheet of water, beyond which cows were moving slowly across a meadow. There were trees about them with homing birds soaring and sinking. In front a white Georgian house, flaunting its Corinthian columns and peristyle, stood inscrutable, flanked by a miscellany of undistinguished wings, and a Gothic chapel. Mother Lehon's warm heart sank. This, after the magnificence of old Marmoutier and its spacious new buildings! What a hovel of a place in spite of its brave façade! Instead of the sky-soaring dreams of saints, with their impress of eternity, there lingered still traces of the worldly ambitions of money-making men clinging to the things of time. She looked again at her companion, then leaned forward, touching her knee gently. *"Benedicta qui venit in nomine Domini,"* she said quietly.

The carriage stopped and they climbed out, while the nuns gathered round. Old and young, they were to be Mother Digby's new daughters because she came to them in the name of the Lord.

Chapter Nineteen

1872

MOTHER LEHON had returned to France. "It is quite right to feel sacrifices," she had said, "but make them in a spirit which is great, gay and generous."

To be not only superior of a house, but also superior of a

vicariate, even if that vicariate as yet numbered just four houses, to be in charge of novices, too, even if there were only four novices, those were sacrifices to be accepted, though for the time the burden seemed crushing. Mother Digby stood in the central vestibule of the old Georgian house, as though in the center of her work beginning here in England, and felt in the silence its life surge round her.

The wide gracious sweep of the staircase leading up to the circular room where the novices sat working was the setting for ladies in stiff brocades squired by the fashionable gentlemen of the Prince Regent's company. The Adam fireplaces, the moulded ceilings where a great hooked-beaked plaster eagle spread his wings, the trellised walls where painted butterflies fluttered among painted blossoms, tall mirrors and illusory perspectives, there were the contributions to the art of living, of Mr. Benjamin Goldsmid, kindly money lender, glad that the future George IV should dance in his ballroom and that the aristocracy should eat his superb meals. Up and down that large room on her left, watched by the adoring eyes of little Lionel Goldsmid, Nelson had walked the morning before he left for Trafalgar, and had told the boy to look well and see what a funny-looking fellow he was, armless in naval coat, white breeches with naval buttons at the knee, and wrinkled stockings above his large buckled shoes. The nuns had made the room into a chapel on their arrival and the first Mass had been celebrated there on the Feast of the Immaculate Heart of Mary in 1851. Now children learned deportment in it and made their curtsies as the list of their achievements for the week was read out with due solemnity.

Mother Digby went out into the yard behind. There was an opening that led down into the cellars. She descended and examined the arching and the slant of the passages. Surely this was something older than the Georgian superstructure, vestigial remains of others who had lived and gone about their daily round of work, and loved and suffered, and were now forgotten. Life must be something other than bricks and mortar, too frail monuments for the soul of man. Overhead was the solid work of the Eighteenth Century. How long would it stand? How many years would pass before its superstructure was rubble? Already other princes and great men had moved through its rooms, building a house not made with hands—Cardinal Wiseman, the saintly Bishop Grant, the Passionist Father Ignatius Spencer, Father de Smet, with his tales of the Rocky Mountains and his witness to the holiness of Mother Duchesne. They were the master masons, but she, too, had her part in this raising of the New Jerusalem in England's green and pleasant land.

Across the yard were the workshops of the carpenter and gardeners. Their work would always be needed. She looked at the new house running back from the lane across the open space of yard. Heavy, substantial, no architectural achievement, it was yet useful for the community and the twenty-three orphans. There were two of the girls watching her now, hoydenish and giggling, one Catholic, one not. It was a pity they were not given into the charge of the nuns sooner, before the bad habits of their early upbringing had cut deep into their characters. She thought of the tales of disappointment that had been told her, and wondered if they were the right persons to be undertaking this work. She had no doubts about the five or six village children who came to the free school. The nuns had the grace to teach them. That was a work which must grow.

She walked to the west end of the building that had been added in 1855 to the Georgian house, and, skirting it, came out upon the front terrace. Above the portico of the wing, hands joined, eyes cast down, stood the statue of Mary, conceived without sin, raised on the crescent moon, her foot on the serpent's head. She read the legend that ran across the frontage: *"Immaculata Beatae Mariae Virginis Conceptio sit nobis Praesidium et Protectio."* It was a joy to think that this house was dedicated in so special a way to the Immaculate Conception. That would be the safeguard of these young girls who came to this place for their education. What must the nuns give them? Not only the piety and innocent happiness of their years at boarding school, but also the strength of principles which would prepare them to fight against the difficulties of life and the lure of pleasure. They must be shown that the only source of happiness was self-mastery, which would ensure their future as Christians and be the joy of their families. There must be strong studies according to the spirit of the Plan their Foundress had conceived, careful preparatory reading on the part of the nuns and the same exacted from the children, all carried out with an earnestness that expanded the intelligence and endowed the mind with sound and steady principles to guide the will and keep the heart for God. Yes, all these were required if they were to be educators of youth . . . youth so inclined to mistake the pretty for the beautiful, and the interesting for the true. To educate was not to keep children quiet or amuse them. It was to take possession in God's name of each of their faculties, and of every talent, and lead them to rise above the weaknesses of childhood, and return with usury to their Creator and Lord. "Thou hast given me five talents; here, Lord, are other five."

There were flowers bright in the beds along the terrace. Below, the sunken Italian garden of former days had changed into a simple grass plot. It might be possible to play croquet here and cricket and the games that English children loved. English children . . . the Franco-Prussian war had brought too many foreign girls among the seventy that would be coming back for the Christmas term. The love of the Sacred Heart was one, but nation differed from nation in outward manifestations. What a garden this would be for hide-and-seek! She walked down the path through the shrubberies and along the acacia avenue. The stone dryads and fauns of the garden's first glory had gone. St. Joseph smiled benignly from the shelter of rhododendron bushes. At the extreme edge, a mound, tree-embowered, was covered with stone slabs. She read the inscriptions. Here were buried the dogs and cats dear to the former owners. Curious, but scarcely worth preserving. In her mind's eye she saw the mound surmounted by a Calvary.

She went into the enclosed garden. A few wind-blown snap-dragons waved on the crannied summit of its green-weathered red brick walls. Plum trees and pears stretched their arms against them and she caught sight of the red and golden fruit. There was a gardener at work among the low box hedge that framed the paths. He stood up at her approach and touched his cap.

"Good morning to you, Reverend Mother. This'll be your first look around the garden? Yes, there's a fine crop of apples. A lot of windfalls on the ground already, and the wasps at 'em."

"I'll bring the novices out to gather them up," she suggested. "There is a great deal of work in the garden."

"Thirty-six acres of it," he said, "counting the meadow. I do it myself with a boy or so to help. It's not what it was . . . twenty gardeners were here when old Goldsmid had the place, and Lord Ellenborough after him. It's seen some changes since then. Why, I've had Bishop Morris, him that was a Bene-dictine and chaplain here for thirty years, with a besom in his hand sweeping the leaves up in the drive. I'd not put it past Father Robertson either. He's a nice gentleman; they say he came into the Church through finding a second-hand breviary on a bookstall. He's worn himself out among the poor Catholics at Greenwich. I'm glad the nuns are giving him a rest, now. I reckon these converts deserve it."

Converts. They had been speaking of them to her as though indeed a Second Spring was at hand. They were coming into the Church from every level of society, from every walk of life. There were contacts with the Children of Mary of the world, with the poor who came for help, with work people and with those whose approach, unexpected and inexplicable, was a very leading of God. As she walked back to the house, she remembered long ago in Marmoutier, before the breaking of dawn, when she was only Mistress of Discipline, her door had been opened suddenly and the novice Cecil Kerr had burst in on her and had cried out, "I've been thinking that neither you nor I pray half enough for the conversion of England."

She paused on the terrace and looked down through the trees to the soft blue hills stretching out to Hampstead, Highgate, and beyond to the heart of England, northward still through the shires to the Border and the whole untouched realm of Scotland. Three houses across the Irish Channel, but only this one lying behind her to be the torch to lead the people of this land back to the understanding their forefathers had of the Wound in the Heart of Christ. What a precious trust, the Heart of Christ, laid in their weak hands, so that no flesh should glorify itself in His presence! It included all devotions since It was their source . . . a Bread containing in Itself all sweetness . . . inexhaustible riches . . . devotion to the Incarnation . . . to the love, sorrows, and wounds of Christ . . . to His Sacred Passion, to the Holy Eucharist . . . to the whole of His Inner Life. By this sign would they triumph over their enemies, and lead the children to their everlasting blessedness.

She went in at the door in the strangers' cloister and into the side chapel. Through the arch that gave on to the sanctuary, she saw the tabernacle set in the stone splendors of the High Altar, beneath the vaulted roof. Then she turned her eyes to the gleaming white statues above the side altar. Blessed

Margaret Mary knelt with clasped hands before Christ who unveiled His Heart to her. What else mattered? That was the fund from which with all confidence she could draw all graces needed for herself and the souls confided to her care. She was a steward of His treasure.

Mother Kieran was waiting for her as she came out. "I hope you like the chapel, Reverend Mother," she said. "The first stone was laid and blessed by Bishop Morris on July 3rd, 1852. You would be surprised how quickly it rose. A Protestant neighbor gave us a very substantial sum toward it, and by June 30th the next year it was ready to be blessed and Bishop Grant came for the High Mass. We added the sacristy, lodge and cloisters a couple of years later, and the Chapel of the Sacred Heart was finished only in 1868. Mother Lucy Worswick asked her family to decorate it . . . her last request to them as she lay dying. That was the year we had the first Corpus Christi procession in the garden. There were only fifty children and the twenty-two orphans, but it was something. That year, too, we helped Bishop Grant with the first Church of the Sacred Heart, in Camberwell."

The portress summoned Mother Digby to the parlor. Lady Georgiana Fullerton wished to greet the new superior on behalf of the Children of Mary of the world.

As she opened the door, Reverend Mother Digby saw only the lady's maid in severe dark clothes, with unbecoming black bonnet, seated on the chair. She glanced round, wondering if Earl Granville's daughter had moved into the window embrasure. Then a deep melodious voice greeting her made her turn again to the seated figure. Facing those mild eyes, that massive forehead and sensitive mouth, and catching something of the peace and goodness that shone over the plain features, she knew that here was her visitor whose novels had been acclaimed by Gladstone and Lord Brougham. There was no hint of the bluestocking in the smiling face, and she listened entranced to the account Lady Georgiana gave her of the members of the Sodality.

"You need not fear for us, Reverend Mother, so long as we have Father Peter Gallwey, to give our retreats. I still remember his first one as a quite young Jesuit in 1860. He spoke to us of Our Lady: 'She was only Mother of God, while you are great ladies. She went on foot, and you don't want to be seen except in a carriage.' We meet at the convent of the Sisters of Mercy in Blandford Square, as this is so far out. You will meet their children when they come out here in the summer for a treat. They are very kind but we need a central Convent of the Sacred Heart. Mother Barat wanted it . . . Reverend Mother Goetz wanted it when we asked her on her visit two years ago. You could do a lot of good among the poor, too, if you came right in to London."

There was another visitor waiting to pay her respects. Large and breathless, Mrs. Robinson shook Mother Digby's hand with vigor.

"I had to come to welcome you, for the Friends of the Sacred Heart. We're that grateful to be able to come here for our meetings and to learn more about Our Lord. We've a pretty hard life, Reverend Mother. It's scrubbing floors most days for me, and me with bronchitis, so that I don't get much time for prayers. But I know now how to arrange it all with Him. When I get all choked up, I say to Him, 'This'll be for you, dear Lord.' And then we know that we can always get help here if we're right off work. And peace and quiet for an hour or so in the chapel. So I had to come in and say how do. I'll not keep you now. May the joys of heaven be your reward, all the Saints of Paradise be your guardians, and the Sacred Heart be your resting place all through the night."

With a bow, Mrs. Robinson went through the doorway. Mother Digby heard her plodding along the strangers' cloister, and then the outer door closed on her. She walked back to the central vestibule and mounted the wide staircase to her own little room. Yes, she knew now something of the work before her and the responsibility that was hers in it. Hers! Then it was as if suddenly she saw herself in the searing light of the sanctity of God . . . worthless, weak, with no virtue or holiness, abysmal nothing before the All. She felt an overwhelming desire to proclaim her worthlessness aloud, to let her community know what kind of thing they had for a superior.

But wasn't it enough to know that the Heart of her Lord held the secret of all her days, and He could not fail in wisdom, power or love and was never more close than in the time of trial? She went into her room and sat down at her desk, already covered with correspondence. A sharp stabbing pain in her temple told her that one of her headaches was beginning.

Chapter Twenty

1872

"Y o u know, Reverend Mother, that I could never hold the children at the Trinità."

Mother Digby looked down at the eager face of the speaker. The bright blue eyes were clouded now with earnestness, the transparent cheeks flushed. But there was the spirit of Scottish chivalry in Mother Henrietta Kerr, and Mother Digby smiled at this Mistress General whom Reverend Mother Goetz had sent her straight from her profession. Here was the background that would give her those qualities that children needed: memories of a happy family life with lively brothers, of a father who set his quest of the truth above the possession of a comfortable benefice, of a mother who took ill-health in her stride; a life of thought and reflection, of interest in the happenings of the day and in the great books of all times; learning carried lightly and music part of its essential graciousness.

"English children are not the same as fiery little Italians," she said, knowing that they would appreciate at least Mother Kerr's straight sincerity. "You know what our Mother Foundress expected of the Mistress General. You must see to it that they study well and play well. Start off with religion . . . she called it the only science whose object is eternal. There is your center. Then they will have some elementary notions of philosophy; with the growing knowledge of themselves, you will put them in possession of the great principles which are a guide to life and which will ensure an indestructible basis for truth as well as morality. You must teach your class mistresses to stimulate thought by skillfully framed questions, and develop the judgment of the children. Don't forget that the class mistresses are mothers to their children, not pedagogues . . . they will take from the class mistress their appreciations, their taste for serious work, their spirit of order and economy, practical organization, tact, kindness, love of books in which they will find great writers' wealth of thought and its peculiar power of opening up further trains of thought. Literature and History—those are formative subjects."

She turned to her desk and reached for a little book. "Listen to what our Mother wrote in her Plan of Studies in 1850. 'Those to whom they are entrusted must . . . strive to strengthen the children in faith, virtue, and in the love of what is true, right and good . . . and profit by every opportunity of forming their minds, their judgments and their hearts.' And again, hear her desire that we should make Religion, Faith and the Kingdom of the Heart of Jesus grow throughout the world by means of these children who will be the women, the wives and the mothers of tomorrow."

"And we must do this by teaching them as well, Latin, Mathematics, Geography, Astronomy," said Mother Kerr, and added, "Well, there are fields there to make us admire the marvelous works of God. No wonder we need much prayer in our lives."

"Not quite like the Carmelites, because we have to descend into the arena, to fight on the field of battle of education, where the friends and enemies of God meet to struggle for the souls of children. But you mustn't have any fear. There are people who are always doubting and asking, 'Is this right, is this wrong, to do this or not to do that?' It is always right to give yourself, to make God's Will your center without any reserve or any delay."

"And His Will is that I should be Mistress General," answered Mother Kerr. "It is a great undertaking."

"Which will mean plenty of mortification, death to self, and suffering. But you don't buy jewels with half-pennies. You must pay the price. Suffering . . . our life ought to be marked with it as Our Lord's was. But for goodness' sake, Mother, don't be always feeling your pulse and administering to yourself homoeopathic doses of suffering."

Mother Charlotte Leslie, passing down the corridor, wondered what the Superior and the Mistress General were laughing about. It was good to hear Reverend Mother Digby's merriment about the house as in the happy days when she was with her at Marmoutier. It was interesting to find God weaving diverse threads in and out of life. It was at Marmoutier in 1860 that Miss Henrietta Kerr made a retreat and learned to know the Society. She had met Reverend Mother

Barat once and had asked her to make a foundation in Scotland. Mother Leslie had been praying long for that very thing. And now here they were all together again in an English house, at the beginning surely of a new era. It was exciting to feel oneself part of God's great scheme.

The children were all back punctually for the September opening of term. Mother Digby took Mother Kerr down to the assembly room to introduce the new Mistress General. The eighty children ranged in a semicircle rose, curtsied and sat down again, eyeing curiously the short form of the new superior. They listened in silence while she named Mother Kerr. Then she went on: "As you have all come back so punctually, we shall have a holiday for the school tomorrow. There will be picnics with your class mistresses and games in the garden."

There was a wriggle of delight in the ranks of the smallest children. One of the older girls in the First Class turned and looked coldly at the twelve-year-olds who were beginning to smile with delight. The silence grew. Then a spokesman stood up in the midst of the First Class girls. Almost contemptuously she looked down at Mother Digby, and pulling herself to her full height, in pained tones she said, "Reverend Mother, in view of the recent loss of our superior and Mistress General, Mother Goold, who, you say, is in France and not coming back to us, we couldn't possibly enjoy ourselves. May I ask, therefore, in the name of all the school, to decline the holiday?"

Mother Kerr glanced sideways at Mother Digby. She caught the quick glint of a twinkle in her eyes. Then her words came with the utmost courteous solemnity, "Why, certainly, if you so wish it. You are entirely free to spend the day in study if you prefer it. There will be the picnic and games for those who want, but you certainly need not take part."

She left them in dignified silence like their own, noting that the feet of the lower classes were shuffling uncomfortably. There was to be no pressure. The choice of the children was their own. But in the mild September sunshine the next day, there was many a game of hide-and-seek among the golden fallen leaves, and the First Class, sitting with study books open before them, could hear merry laughter and catch glimpses of happy groups, apples in hands, recounting their exploits to the new Superior and the new Mistress General. It was very hard not to enjoy oneself with them.

Mother Phillips came to Reverend Mother in distress. "I can't keep order in my class, I know, however hard I try. I do prepare my lessons, I know my matter, but the older girls just aren't interested. Today they have refused to do the exercise I set."

"Send the girls to me," said Mother Digby grimly. They came, the little group of disaffected girls, ready to laugh at the situation, and to get their way as they had over the holiday. They caught the blaze in the deep blue eyes that seemed to read right down into them, and they were afraid. The quiet tones cut into their self-satisfaction.

"I have no desire for a large school, unless each one in it understands her duty. You are here to learn. The mistresses stand for authority. You are failing in your duty unless you recognize these facts. You have a responsibility to the others in the school, to your parents, to yourselves. If you do not fulfil your duty, I shall return you to your parents."

That night, the exercises were laid on Mother Phillips' table.

"The school is finding itself," said Mother Kerr in the new year. "It's a different place. It's getting to feel like a family of the Sacred Heart . . . but there are still many faults to correct."

Mother Digby reflected.

"Two faults I fear above all others in children: want of straightness, and levity. Such characters haven't even the capacity of a cream cheese for receiving an impression. You will have to lay deep principles in their minds. You will have to suffer for them, Mother. But that is a good thing, one of the beatitudes Our Lord spoke of. You will have to take yourself in hand, too. You won't expect me to put a poultice on your self-love!"

"I wish we had a copy of the picture of Mater Admirabilis at the Trinità," said Mother Kerr. "Our Lady has given that specially to help children."

"Why don't you get one of the girls to attempt it? Mary has had a good deal of training, and she would put prayer into the task."

The large canvas awed the girl, but she set to work. The Art Master came, a little sceptical, to give his advice, but as the weeks passed by, he watched with astonishment her growing skill and mastery. Old Protestant that he was, he began to be fascinated by the little Madonna in her pink dress, and was as anxious as the copyist that the finished work should be good.

"There's something about her," he said. "It's not a good piece of drawing even in the original, and the colors are really all wrong. But she's right for these children. She's their age, I suppose, and she's showing them how to work at a woman's job with her spindle and distaff, and to study with her open book and to be pure of heart with the lily beside her. I'd like to know the thoughts behind those lowered eyelids."

The picture was set up in the circular entrance hall of the old Georgian house where now the Children of Mary had their chapel. Two lamps were set burning beside her. The children began to find their way to her in all their joys and difficulties. Mother Kerr watched them.

"Teach them after your example," she prayed, "to give all that they may find all, to trust God in all things as their best friend and to be fully convinced that He is too merciful, too loving and too just to be outdone in generosity."

Mother Digby watched the secret smile on the lips of Mater Admirabilis.

"Our Lady," she said softly. "In dangers, hours of difficulties, temptations, trials . . . our remedy. Invoke her, look to her as to your Star. She will always be the straight road, true and short, the perfect way that will lead you always to Our Lord. Let your trust in her be without bounds. I trusted everything to her from the first moment of my religious life, so that she would be the guardian of all the treasures that were being given to me, to bring them forth when the need arose. She has always been faithful, reminding me of what I needed to strengthen me or show me the way at every turn of my life. *Monstra te esse Matrem*."

A Mother . . . That was what growing girls needed. Of school she would make a home.

Chapter Twenty-one

1873

A s the cab jolted its way from Archbishop's House, Westminster, Mr. Allies went over the events of the past year, seeking some way to put his message less unpalatably to the Superior Vicar of the Nuns of the Sacred Heart. True, he had got to know her well enough to be sure that she would accept it as coming from authority, which was for her the Providence of God, but on a bleak December day, Archbishop Manning's words were even bleaker. Father Gallwey had said to him, "A fine Christmas present you are taking her from the Holy Child!"—and he had to agree grimly—and yet, where had she failed to be anything but wise and humble?

The matter had begun in the December of 1872, when a friend found a house in Dorset Street just suited for a Convent where the nuns could run a day school, a school for the poor, and have a central meeting place for the Children of Mary. The priests of the parish had rejoiced. Children of every class swarmed in the neighborhood and their schools were all too insufficient. But the Archbishop had delayed in giving his consent, and finally had refused, suggesting that there were already too many convents in the district. One of them was going to open a training college. Mother Digby had offered to hand over the house to the nuns, but again there had been delay and the house was re-sold. Then in the January of this year the Children of Mary had approached the Archbishop and had at length convinced him that Reverend Mother Digby was willing to devote herself to the spiritual needs of his flock in whatever way he wished, and would open a poor school in whatever part of his diocese he wanted. "If so," he had said, "I will bless them with both hands."

That was where he, T. W. Allies, had come into the picture. He sighed as he thought of the wearying task he had undertaken since he had been appointed secretary to the Poor School Committee ten years ago. The Men's Training College at Hammersmith was progressing, so was the Notre Dame Training College for Women at Liverpool, but the beggarly grants that came from Mr. Lowe's Revised Code with the strain that it imposed on the college authorities had caused shipwreck to the Holy Child nuns' college at St. Leonard's on Sea. Why should grants for students be deferred until after they had left college and be paid only if they received from their schools two twelve-monthly reports that were favorable? It was hard enough first to find sufficient girls able to take the four-year course as pupil teachers before entering for the Queen's Scholars examination for entry, and then with enough apostolic zeal to be willing to work for a salary of £26 per annum. Yet teachers were in key positions, and their education demanded the best that could be obtained. There was no sound education without religion; as was the teacher, so was the child; as was the trainer, so was the teacher. The Committee had wanted the nuns of the Sacred Heart to undertake the work. It had been put to the Bishops. Bishop Ullathorne had given the casting vote, to the joy of the clergy.

Mother Digby had prayed much about the matter before accepting the idea with the consent of her Mother House. She had been negotiating all the summer with the Archbishop, who had consecrated his diocese this year to the Sacred Heart. He had asked to see her and had been pleased with her readiness to undertake an orphanage in the central part of London to help him save the faith of so many destitute children, but again he had procrastinated and no answer had come from him. In November she had definitely accepted the request of the Committee to undertake the training college. She had found, too, that the house in Dorset Street could be bought back. Since Mr. Allies was secretary she had written to let him know, and on December 1st he had called on the Archbishop. He surely had not misunderstood His Grace. Surely the permission needed had been given. With time pressing, he had at once made overtures for the house and had sent Her Majesty's Inspectors to report on it. The good-sized rooms, the garden around, the central position, the poor schools at hand, all had met with their approval. And today there had been this fresh summons to the Archbishop's House, and the message which he was even now bearing to Roehampton.

The mudbanks of the river looked desolate, the tide running sluggishly. The cab crossed the misty stream, jogged along deserted roads and between the yellowing grass and damp furze bushes of Barnes Common. At the convent door

135

he paid the driver and rang the bell. Even the smiling face of the portress did not lift the gloom from his heart. In the parlor he laid down his top hat and gloves. His mind was made up. There was no need to wrap up unpalatable news for anyone of the caliber of Mother Digby. When she came into the room, he gave his message. "Reverend Mother, His Grace has informed me today that I have made a grievous mistake in going ahead with Dorset Street. He is unwilling to take upon himself the odium of a direct refusal, but it is quite definite that he will not tolerate you in Dorset Street, or, for that matter, anywhere in his diocese. Don't ask me why. In Rome he loved your order at the Trinità. He is a man of strong prejudices. He will not change. This means the end of your training college in Westminster."

There was a tightening of the lines of Mother Digby's mouth, a lowering of her eyes, a moment's pause. But he saw no disturbance in the calm of her face.

"I have wondered, Mr. Allies, whether this opposition is a sign that God does not want us in Westminster, or whether it is just the cross that prepares the fruit. How hard, how much harder than all besides, it is to bear persecution from the friends of God."

That was all. She was silent, turning things over still in her mind.

"What of the students you have accepted for February?" he asked in anxiety. "They will be lost to the Catholic cause . . . if they train at all, it will be in Protestant colleges."

Her deep eyes looked straight at him. "No, Mr. Allies, not that. If we can get Bishop Danell's consent, we will have a training college in this diocese of Southwark. But I shall leave this entirely to you and the Poor School Committee."

"You must pray, Reverend Mother. It is more than three years now since Mr. Forster's Education Act opened the door to universal and free education, and Catholic schools must be built and staffed as quickly as possible if we are not to lose our Catholic children."

"Mr. Allies, our Mother Foundress when she was young had a desire to found an order where her nuns should be adorers of the Sacred Heart in His gift of the Blessed Sacrament. She saw that if they taught children, the number of these adorers would be increased greatly. She allowed her daughters for the same reason to teach at Pigneroles the young girls of the neighborhood who in their turn taught the children in outlying districts of the neighborhood, which the nuns could never reach. This work of training teachers, even with all that it involves of examinations and government inspection, is one after her own heart. It will pass the love of the Sacred Heart ever outward to thousands upon thousands of children. You will find it will come about in spite of my clumsy dealings and real incapacity for business."

He gathered up his hat and gloves. Incapacity! He wished she could hear what priests and members of the Committee were saying about her. Yes, he knew that the work was in the right hands and that the poor children whom His Grace the Archbishop loved so dearly would get help from the Sacred Heart. As he walked out into the gathering dank mist under the heavy trees, the gloom was no longer in his heart. He would tell the Committee as soon as possible how things stood.

Not until January 23rd did the Committee decide finally that the training college should be in Southwark. Mother Digby received the news and acted promptly. She called Mother Kerr and Mother Leslie. "This will mean another house, when we can get it. That means that I shall have to go immediately to Paris to arrange for the community to live in it. We must know something about the running of a training college. I am sending Mothers Phillips, Laprimaudaye and Power to see the Mount Pleasant College at Liverpool.

137

They will only get hooted at if they travel in their habits. Dress them like Helpers of the Holy Souls in widow's black bonnets and dresses. You have tomorrow to experiment with their costume, then on Monday they can set off. I shall leave at 6:30 for the Mother House."

Late on the next Thursday Mother Digby returned from Paris, cold and tired. She smiled her slow smile as Mother Kerr and Mother Leslie came to her.

"For the new house," she said, "there will have to be changes. You, Mother Kerr, will be assistant here as well as Mistress General and you, Mother Leslie, will be the new superior, with Mother Laprimaudaye as Vice-Principal, and Mother Kieran, Mother Phillips and Mother Power to help in the College. I'm sorry, Mothers. All the peace and joy of religious life is at an end for you, but you will have the opportunity of doing more good and suffering more."

There was a silence. What could one say when God asked sacrifices and one gave them? Then Mother Kerr's laugh broke out.

"I think we had all better kiss one another, Reverend Mother," she said. It was what you did to children to ease their pain.

Next day Mother Leslie went to Reverend Mother Digby. "Don't you think I had better go and see what a training college is like, if I am to be Principal?"

Mother Digby looked at her watch. "Go to the linen room and get one of the black bonnets they made for the others. Mother Kieran will get you a cab. You will be just in time to catch the express for Liverpool."

Strategist and tactician, thought Mother Leslie. It was many years since she had been outside the enclosure of Roehampton, but, when Mabel Digby expected it, she knew she could accomplish the plan, her small part of the whole campaign. There was the real leader's genius for getting others to do what was required, and doing it with something of the leader's own spirited humor.

Mother Digby was there to greet their return.

"We are simply bursting with knowledge," cried Mother Laprimaudaye, fingering her notebooks.

"And full of zeal," said Mother Power.

"What news of a house?" asked Mother Leslie.

"The Bishop has not written about one," said Reverend Mother Digby. "We have nowhere yet."

The faces of the College staff fell.

"You will have to get yourselves ready instead," remarked Mother Digby. "You will have to study seriously for the South Kensington examinations."

"Come along," said Mother Laprimaudaye. "We'll put out all our books in the room next door ready to begin after Mass tomorrow."

"Look at this," said Mother Digby to Mother Leslie, as she looked over the post next day. "The Bishop and Mr. Allies have decided that we must admit the Queen's Scholars not taken by Liverpool next Saturday, if the Government Inspector will approve of our arrangements. Come and see what we can do."

She had tucked up her habit and made for the orphanage building. "We can turn the orphans' dormitory into their sleeping quarters. Our refectory can be their classroom, the two rooms next to it their refectory and work-room. Bring your Sisters along to help, Mother. The Inspector is coming in two days' time so we have none to lose."

Canon Tinling arrived to inspect the premises. He noted the rooms were simple and clean, with little superfluous furniture. He found the little school at work with one of the nuns and was pleased with their responses to his questions. This place would certainly do temporarily; until such time as they could acquire a proper house, they would be allowed to take twenty-two students. They should arrive by February 21st, and a Government grant would be available when the premises were ready. He thought, however, that it would be difficult for the girls to be collected from their scattered homes in the time. He wished Reverend Mother success in the work.

"Now we can get on with our study," said Mother Power, as she saw that all the material arrangements were ready on the Saturday.

"Reverend Mother, Reverend Mother," cried Mother Phillips in great excitement coming from the lodge, "they're here. Our first students are here!"

Mother Digby went down to greet them, her welcoming kind smile warming them as they stood a little desolate on the threshold of their new career: Annie Sargent from Maidstone, Grace Dobell from West Malling, and Hannah Parker from Haverstock Hill.

Chapter Twenty-two

1874

MABEL DIGBY pondered over the College register. Students from distant places: Lanarkshire, Tipperary, Lancashire, Staffordshire; students from near at hand: Wapping, Drury Lane, Mortlake. They would carry the love of the Sacred Heart back with them to their own homes . . . yes, if only they could be trained. But how train them without a college, and how have a college without a house? The Bishop had not found one. The Government gave them until March 1st. The time was growing short. She decided swiftly and called Mother Leslie.

"I am convinced we shall never get a house unless we take the trouble to look for one ourselves. You must take Mother Kieran with you, and find one. You will have to dress as ladies of the world . . . in the clothes the postulants have discarded," she added with a smile. These fashionable daughters of hers! "You know what the Committee and the Privy Council want. It is to be as near as possible to London, if not in London. You know what the Bishop wants. It is not to be near any existing convent that has schools for the poor. You might try the south-east district round Deptford and Blackheath."

Outside there was white frost silvering every branch and spray under a biting north-east wind, but Reverend Mother Digby's optimism warmed them. Cab rides, smoky trains, the new experience of horse-drawn tramway omnibuses, it was all fun, and they would come back triumphant to hear her "Well done!"

But house agents refused the new villas when they learned they were to be converted into a college, derelict houses were dirty or labyrinthine or ill-ventilated. From Deptford to Blackheath Hill there was nothing, and the short winter day's sun dipped behind the trees in the rising mist as they confessed their failure to each other.

Mother Digby recognized no failure. In the days that followed, she searched Clapham, Clapham Junction, Putney, Battersea, Bolingbroke Grove, with no success. An agent suggested The Orchard on Wandsworth Hill. Mother Kieran and Mother Leslie surveyed the large white house afar off as their cab jogged along the Lower Wandsworth Road by the river.

"Too deserted and too tumble-down," they decided. Anyway, Mr. Allies thought he had at last found just the place they wanted in Putney.

But the Putney house needed too much alteration. Was there any large house left in the south of London they had not seen? And March 1st was very near.

Then, on Ash Wednesday, February 24th, another house agent told them of a place on West Hill, Wandsworth. Mother Leslie went off post haste with Mother Vercruysse. They came back jubilant.

"It's The Orchard, Reverend Mother. Come and see for yourself."

They set off along the heathy common flanked by large houses lying back from the road. Down the hill they went until they drew up at the door of the large empty house. Mr. Allies was there and went around with her, anxious to see if this would suit governmental requirements. She pointed out to him that the rooms were spacious, that there was dignity about their height, that the grounds were extensive and the situation above the river healthy. They looked down the hill to where the old village of Wandsworth was fast disappearing in jerry-built houses that held the families of artisans, builders, and the men who worked on the market-gardens along by the river.

"There will be children here," she said, and her eyes followed the course of the river and noted the clustering hovels that sprawled outwards from Battersea and crept up the valley of the Wandle.

"The streets just below you there," said Mr. Allies, "are some of the worst in this part of the metropolis. There are gipsy encampments, and ne'er-do-wells, and worse, living in tenements. Your students will have much to give. Set up your school here, and you will be as truly a missionary as those who go to Africa. There is no other church or convent in this neighborhood. In that small house down there on this property, the first Mass in these parts after the Reformation was celebrated, they say, but there is no Mass said now. The place is very Protestant."

To open another tabernacle! To give Christ a foothold in a place where He was unknown. To set it between the rich who were too comfortable to want Him, and the poor, who were too neglected! This surely was the house chosen by His Sacred Heart. Again she decided swiftly, and began at once negotiations for its purchase.

Bricks and mortar: she knew well their importance by now, but she knew them as body to spirit. She must infuse soul now into this enterprise. The college staff must be wise with the wisdom of the world. There were the intricacies of school management to study and the emphasis now being put on the physical sciences by the Science and Art Department must not be neglected. There was room for these studies in the integrated Plan of Studies of the Society. She engaged well-known specialists to give her nuns lectures.

"We must devote ourselves to the acquisition of this secular knowledge that is being asked for. We bear the responsibility of giving Catholic children an education equal to that given in non-Catholic schools. If we or our students neglect study and fall below the standard required, parents and children might in consequence resort to schools in which knowledge of God is not taught. Mr. Disraeli has spoken of the 1870 Act as creating a new sacerdotal class . . . the schoolmaster is not for us the substitute for the priest."

Mother D'Arcy and Mother Theresa Neil, the novices destined for teaching in the College, were set to work to pass the South Kensington examinations. Mother Digby was in Paris assisting at the election of Mother Lehon as Mother General when they took them in May, and she laughed over their humble letter with its doleful account of their inefficiency in spite of all their midnight study, disgracing both themselves and the Society in the eyes of the British Government.

"I value the humility of my novices more than their success," she wrote back. God alone knew the truth. What they were worth in His sight, that was their worth, neither more nor less. In the meantime, He was teaching them all patience and a waiting on His good pleasure. The community was living in awkward and restricted quarters; they were happy to offer their inconvenience for the success of a work that had so close a connection with the salvation of souls.

The twenty-one students, too, were foundation stones who must be lovingly shaped to the pattern of Christ Himself. Home from Paris in June, Mother Digby paused in the Strangers' Cloister and looked back. The heavy wooden door of the Chapel of the Sacred Heart was open wide, and through its framework she could see them kneeling in prayer. They had lighted candles on the altar but the mellow sunset of the summer evening was striking through the window to the left and making the white statue of Our Lord glow golden. This was the Feast of His Sacred Heart and He had answered their prayers after long waiting. Today the contract for the purchase of The Orchard had been signed; they could take possession legally on June 24th. She had spoken to the students on this their first Feast Day, giving them each a picture of the Sacred Heart and a medal of Mater Admirabilis. She prayed that, in the years to come, these two loves would be their safeguard in all their trials and the sign by which they would conquer the world for God. They were singing a hymn now, their whole soul going into their voices. What splendid material here to do His work! There was silence; then she heard them take up an invocation:

Sacred Heart of Jesus, I trust in Thee!
Sacred Heart of Jesus, I believe in Thy love for me!
Sacred Heart of Jesus, may Thy Kingdom come!

She must set Mother Leslie's feet, too, on that impregnable rock of trust. Better that she should go forward alone and win her spurs in dealing with the obdurate late owner who still kept his furniture locked in the best room, and the policeman caretaker who, with his wife and four children, refused to move out. She was there behind her daughter to approve her selling the crop of hay the day before the late owner sent to cut it, her importing carpenters, workmen, sweeps, while the policeman was still in possession, but it was she too who sent delicacies to the caretaker's wife when she gave birth to a fifth child.

On July 20th, her mother's heart had foreseen everything for the exodus from Roehampton. The farm cart was piled high with bedsteads and mattresses, pots, pans and pails, brushes and brooms. Bread from the convent bakehouse and butter from the dairy and cold meat for their day's meals were packed into the cab that took Mother Vercruysse as Mother Assistant with three Sisters. A carriage was ready for Mother Leslie, with Mother Laprimaudaye, Mother Power and Mother Bergel. She waved good-bye to the five students who lived too far away to return home for the holidays, and made sure they had beds for the night. Fanning the gardener trudged across Putney Heath with Patricia, the big black cow, and three calves, and, since there were no locks on any doors and the palings round the property were broken and gaping, at the close of the day Alphonse, the French handyman, slow of thought and no hero, was sent with the little dog of the Roehampton convent to be their bodyguard.

The next day, as soon as the first Mass was over, Mother Digby set off in the carriage herself for West Hill. It was lovely in the early morning, with bird-song and fragrant flowers and resinous trees scenting the air, in a stillness undisturbed by man's business. Her daughters caught sight of her as the horse turned into the drive, and, joyful and laughing, crowded round her to tell her of their first night in the college. No lights, a baby that cried without ceasing, a dog that barked in company, tied to the grate in the kitchen where the valiant Alphonse lurked, a well whose rusty mechanism broke, a fire kindled with sticks gathered in the garden, a dairyman chary about serving them while he tried to decide if they were orphans, widows, or lunatics, Patricia who discovered a skittish youthfulness when Sister Conroy tried to milk her; it was all good fun when Mother Digby's laugh rang out.

They sat round the one available table and laid plans for the day. She produced a picture of the Sacred Heart and a stand for it. She had brought a lamp and lit it and arranged a large bouquet of flowers before it in the empty room that would serve for the time being as a chapel. There would have to be a larger building for the students and the children when the work was under way. Perhaps with a school to build for all the poor children who were even now getting to know of their arrival and clamoring for entrance, they would have to be content for some time with an iron structure. But the time would come when they would have forgotten this poor and humble beginning, and have a chapel more worthy of the Teacher of all teachers. She blessed the little community and returned to Roehampton.

"Don't waver before any difficulties," she said to them as they parted. "Think of all that your Mothers have borne before the foundation of this house and do your part."

Their part. It all lay in recognizing what that was. Her two novices had just learned that they had gained a First and Second Division Pass in the Science and Art Department Examination. The students' quarterly examinations were better, and Mr. Hullah had commended their music when he had inspected them. Her staff were seeing results.

"But they must never let the solid give way to the showy," she reflected. "They must do their best, yes, but cultivate the spirit of thanksgiving. All success must be counted in terms of eternity and the grace of God. Those who work in the college must never forget this. Let them become souls of prayer."

Chapter Twenty-three

1878

MOTHER HENRIETTA KERR was busy writing to the Mother House. "Reverend Mother Digby makes her daughters happy beyond all description. Truly I think it would be difficult to find on this earth a gathering of people more joyful and carefree than are your daughters at Roehampton. The union which reigns there is a taste of that hundredfold which Our Lord has promised even in this life."

She paused, running her mind back over the years. She would have been incapable of managing herself, with her wrist too weak for a strong mouth, the unruly boarding school of 1873. And now, with the older woman's wisdom of experience to guide her and utmost trust to uphold her, she had children who were truly at home in the house. It was all Reverend Mother Digby's doing, and all *she* could do, in return, was to add another burden to her superior by each winter becoming less and less able physically to carry on the work, and requiring those tender ministrations which by rights she should have been giving and not receiving. Perhaps it was something to be Reverend Mother's jester, to say the witty word that set her deep laugh echoing around the recreations, or the wry remark that put the humorous side of hard matters to the fore.

How could you look after someone whose standard of suffering was so high? In the first years they had written to the Mother House to beg Reverend Mother Lehon, now Superior General, to order Mother Digby to take care of herself. They knew of her headaches, guessed at her sleepless nights. There had been the examination by the Paris doctor and his recommendation of a seton to be inserted between her shoulders. Dr. Harper had performed the operation at Roehampton, smiling into her smiling eyes as he prepared for it. He had said, "The more I hurt, the more grateful you will be to me hereafter."

They understood each other, the Englishwoman who laughed when an effusive South American visitor clapped her vigorously upon the back where the open wound was, and the doctor who had seen as in a vision the Precious Blood falling like rain upon the gray streets of London, and who was all night and all day at the beck of the poor without a murmur. "She is made for suffering," Dr. Harper had said of Mother Digby, and Father Gallwey had said of him, "His serenity of character is a sublime endowment." And the strength of both lay in the Mass. But these last months, even Reverend Mother's courage had not been able to overcome the exhaustion that beset her. They must write again to the Mother House to urge that she should be given rest. When everyone else in the Infirmary was cared for tenderly, she alone was not looked after. With a pain at her heart, Mother Kerr realized that Reverend Mother Digby thought that all care would be wasted; her days were numbered. Still . . . she picked up her pen and began again.

The priest from Acton was waiting in the parlor. Outside the March wind was blowing great gusts that made the black branches of the trees creak and groan. But within, the warm fire was comforting, comforting as the welcome he had received when he came for help from the Mother Superior. She was even now upstairs getting him the altar linen and vestment that he had asked for to help with the first Mass in the new church on the following Sunday. Yes, she had quite obviously meant it was a joy to give something for a new tabernacle to be opened at Berrymead, the place that had first welcomed the Sacred Heart and where the Holy Sacrifice had not been offered since they had moved from the house to come to Roehampton.

In the sacristy, Mother Digby went to the massive oak cupboard that held the vestments. In the top shelf she knew there was a store of linen and she would be able to satisfy all the priest's requirements. She pulled out the drawer, intending to lift it down on to the table so that she could choose what was necessary. It slid out easily enough on to her upraised hands, but too late she found she could not support its weight . . . It slanted forward, striking her head as it fell. For a moment the pain was intense, and she staggered for support. Then she pulled herself together, gathering up the altar linen that had spilled out. She made her selection, on her knees by the drawer, and the sacristan, coming in, replaced it with her help. The parcel was made up and delivered to the grateful priest, and she returned to her own room to continue her business.

An hour later, it seemed to her that the daylight was fading early. She could scarcely see the address on a letter, though it was only four o'clock. She rose to go nearer to the window, and violent pains shot through her head. All her strength was draining from her. She would have to rest a little.

Dr. Harper came in haste. There was severe concussion, so severe that death within a few days was a possibility. The room was darkened while the fever held her and the agony racked her head. The days passed. She would not die, but her right eye was blind and she could see only dimly with the other. But she was herself again, smiling at the pain, dictating letters of thanks to those who had prayed for her and accusing herself of clumsiness when Reverend Mother Lehon sent her a loving blessing.

"The buds are coming out on the elms," said Mother Kerr in mid-April.

"Yes," said Reverend Mother Digby, "I think I can begin to see them."

Her sight came back, and her active mind took up again the burden of responsibilities, but the doctor shook his head when he saw that day after day she had no strength to stand or walk.

"It is paralysis of both legs, Reverend Mother," he said, without beating about the bush. "You will have to offer that powerlessness for souls. I can mend you so that you can go about on crutches, but the rest is beyond medical skill."

Mother Kerr's militant spirit was not satisfied.

"If doctors can do nothing, we must ask heaven," she said. Novena followed novena, but heaven seemed deaf. Reverend Mother Digby went on with her work, struggling on her crutches to all the Community gatherings, encouraging her daughters, guiding the novices, bringing joy to everyone. They would take her out in the garden in a bath chair, hoping that the freshness of early summer and the warm sun would effect a cure. The robins found her out, as she sat carving the little wooden signals for the class mistresses. They perched upon wheels, upon the rug around her legs. Greatly daring, they alighted upon her head. June passed into July. The little family of robins reared in the wood-shed had been duly brought to be shown off, had eaten cheese from her hand, and had taken their flight.

It had been a busy year in spite of everything. The new novitiate building had been finished, extending the wing where the orphans had been lodged. They had gone this year, and their place had been taken by a growing poor school, where little boys sat on the benches and learnt the Three R's. Their playtime shouts came to her as she sat planning for their future. The eve of this Pentecost, for the first time, they had been able to have the Forty Hours' devotion here. They had carried it through with all possible solemnity. On the first day the Community had sung the Mass, on the second, the students from Wandsworth, while the Jesuit novices had come down the road from Manresa to sing for the third day. It was good to have been allowed to give so much honor to Our Lord in the Blessed Sacrament. She was ready to sing her Nunc Dimittis now, with the last joy that had just come in Reverend Mother Lehon's letter, telling them that their Mother Foundress had been proclaimed Venerable by Holy Church. Soon the August sun would be scorching the green grass, the swallows would be lining up on the railings and fences for their winter flight, the conkers and acorns would be falling from the trees among the dead leaves swept up for burning.

Mother Kerr watched her superior growing weaker as the year drew to its close. Love was not deceived by the gaiety that went with an increase in the pain of headaches. Heaven must listen. Reverend Mother General had asked that December 12th, the centenary of the birth of Mother Barat, should, this year of her public recognition as Venerable, be kept with special family joy. Very well, then, they would start another novena to end on that day. And it should be linked with the Blessed Sacrament. Each day Mass should be offered for the intention of Reverend Mother Digby's cure through the intercession of Venerable Madeleine Sophie Barat, and between the two elevations, all hearts should be lifted to God in union with His Son's. The Mother House was with them and all the Houses of England and Ireland.

It was disappointing that Reverend Mother was so ill again,

so that they could not even see her moving around on her crutches. The children of the school prayed earnestly, but Mother Kerr kept from them the truth that, as the novena progressed, the invalid was becoming weaker.

"I will not join in your petitions," she said, thinking that God could not need so worthless a person as she for His work.

"It's rash to besiege heaven any further," said the Mother Infirmarian on the night of the eighth day. "God has shown His hand. He is asking us for prayers so that her last passage to Him shall be blessed."

Mother Kerr shook her head; with death in her heart, she went down to the school to remind the children to pray fervently on the morrow.

At eleven at night, the infirmarian wondered whether she should not call the priest for the Last Anointings. For an hour the pains in Mother Digby's head were acute. At three, Mother Kerr slipped quietly into the room. She met Mother Digby's bright eyes, saw her smile and shake her head. At five, she tiptoed in again. Still those deep-blue eyes were open, watching her. A spasm of pain passed over her face as she said softly to the Mistress General, "I am no better. What a disappointment for the children!"

At five, the pain had lessened and she began to make her preparation for Holy Communion. Suddenly she said to Mother Kerr, "Take my crutches. Put them at the end of my bed so that Our Lord can see them. If He wills, He can cure me."

They were there at her feet. Mother Kerr knelt beside her. At half-past six, the tinkle of a little bell drawing nearer told of Christ's approach. The priest laid down his ciborium. In the doorway the candles of two kneeling nuns flickered. He turned with the host uplifted.

"Ecce Agnus Dei!"

152

Mother Digby had received her Lord. There was darkness now in the doorway and the tinkle of the little bell faded in the distance. Mother Kerr left her to make her thanksgiving in silence.

She returned a quarter of an hour later with the Mother Infirmarian. The bright blue eyes were smiling.

"I think I am cured," said Reverend Mother Digby. "Take away my crutches." She rose, standing upright without any assistance. "I shall get dressed. If I hurry I shall be in time for the Community Mass."

There was a great deal of pain in her back, but as she put on her clothes unaided, this died away. She opened her bedroom door and stepped out into the corridor with a firm and rapid tread. There was a little staircase that led down a few steps. She hesitated, swaying for a minute, then walked down steadily along the next corridor and up the stairs that led to the tribune at the back of the chapel. Silently she opened the door, went in quickly and knelt before the balustrade. Below were the children in their benches, the nuns in their stalls, her own at the back, empty. The priest with his servers had come out on to the altar. In the tribune the choir of nuns had gathered. The organist turned in her seat to see that they were all ready. One moment, like the rest of the singers, she remained petrified, gazing at the well-known figure kneeling absorbed in the sight of the tabernacle, then she swiveled round, pulling out the organ stops. The music thundered out, triumphant, jubilant. The singers took up the strains. *"Quid retribuam?"* they sang, till the vault re-echoed. Mother Vercruysse, the Assistant, left her stall and ran upstairs to see what possessed the choir. In a minute she was down again. She seized the arm of the first nun she came to with a grip of iron.

"Reverend Mother has walked to the tribune and is kneeling there perfectly cured."

The news spread through the kneeling throng. At the moment between the two elevations a cry of joy went up to God from all hearts through the Heart of His Son.

The Mothers Councilor hastened to Reverend Mother Digby's room as soon as they could. Mother Kerr asked her to stand, to sit, to move about. There was no question about it: she was as able as they were. Her laughter rang out at the sight of their astonished faces. Already she was looking ten years younger. A clock struck. "Quarter to ten. I shall go down to the children for the distribution of ribbons," she said gaily. On the way down, she ran into the chaplain at the foot of the great staircase. Down on her knees she went for his blessing, while the tears rose to his eyes. He went before her into the room where the school was gathered, and cried out, "Children, a great grace has been granted to this house today!"

Mother Kerr saw her children break their neat rows and jump for joy while they clapped again and again. They laughed and cried and crowded round, seeing for themselves what their Mother Madeleine Sophie Barat had done for them. Fast day or no fast day, the Community wrote it in red letters and laughed with the children.

At its close, Mother Digby wrote to the Mother House, "I come to ask you to bless the new strength God has deigned to grant me, so that I can use it for His glory, with that obedience which is my only way of going to Him."

The weeks passed into months and she went about her work again as before her illness. She seemed to have regained much of her old physical powers, and there was no question of a relapse.

"Will that count as a miracle for Mother Barat's canonization?" a child asked Mother Kerr. She shook her head.

"We've sent her crutches to the shrine at Conflans, where she's buried, but it will count only as a grace, not as a miracle."

She did not tell the child that Mother Digby's headaches had not been cured entirely. They still came upon her. Was it fancy that they seemed worse on Fridays? She spoke to Dr. Harper, hoping he would offer comforting assurance for the future. He looked down at her quizzically.

"You've just been telling me that God blesses everything your Reverend Mother touches. Neither souls nor works are suffering through these headaches. Why should you grudge her this likeness to Our Lord? He wore a crown of thorns," said Philip Harper.

Chapter Twenty-four

1882

"TRAIN them to be strong and supernatural." Reverend Mother Goetz' words had shaped all Mother Digby's dealings with the English novices since Mother General had entrusted them to her on her first coming to Roehampton. The small group of "white veils" had grown in the passing of a decade; all the more reason for praying and working for their true strength and foundations in the realm of faith. In novices lay the future of the Society: they were the legatees of the ideas that had come from the mind of God into the mind of the Mother Foundress. The Mistress of Novices had the responsibility of transmitting those ideas integrally, and of assuring healthy cells in the living organism that embodied them. Each soul was God's choice, responding to His calling and rich with the variety of all His Creation. Souls were not alike. Each was a creature too distinct and individual to be ruled by formulas. Before God, each soul was unique and solitary and demanded a particular study.

What enlightenment of the Holy Spirit she must pray for! When they arrived, how differently they were dowered supernaturally too. There were those who seemed to have very little understanding who yet fulfilled what they saw faithfully; to them grace was given step by step in all its plenitude. There were others whose understanding seemed flooded with light who yet did not correspond with their graces; those were the souls over whom she yearned with anxious care. To all she must give that straight sincerity of purpose which would reach the real meaning of religious life, the following of Christ's call to take up their abode in His Heart, love answering love in the most intimate of unions. He had said, "Live on in My Love," not regarding what they were or even what He had given them, but choosing them to live with Him. Why? The why was simple: it was His love alone. And she was charged before God to help them to make their home in Him.

Mother Digby heard the laughter of novices as they made off down the garden path for their recreation, and then the quiet of the July afternoon settled on the terrace again. Somewhere a pigeon was cooing with monotonous pathos. A late cuckoo called from the fields beyond. The rich foliage of the trees was reflected unstirring in the little lake. Sunshine spread its peace over the house as though to bless the supernatural work that was being accomplished in the annual summer retreat for ladies. Mother Digby pondered again on the message Father Gallwey had sent her: "Tell her that if Miss Stuart offers herself for the noviceship, she is not to be refused. Tell her she is the most complete person I have ever met. After forty years of ministry in London, she will know what that means." She had watched Miss Stuart, convert daughter of an Anglican clergyman, in those few days that she had spent in retreat at Roehampton. She had seen her seriousness, her retiringness, her absorption in prayer. Yes, she did know the worth of Father Gallwey's judgment. The most complete person . . . she had prayed already for Miss Stuart. Of what use was completeness of personality unless it was given wholly to God? To whom much was given, much was required.

Miss Janet Stuart sat on a bench on the terrace. It was the seventh day of the retreat. Earlier in the week she had sat on this same bench and looked round over the garden, wondering if its thirty-three acres would be an unbearable circumscription of her being, hearing the canter of horses down the shady lane and asking herself if she could face the idea of never mounting a horse again. Now things were otherwise. Through the desolation of prayer, she had offered herself unreservedly to follow Christ the King, and the darkness had parted and the chapel and every room at Roehampton had been flooded with light and had echoed glory. The decision had been made on her side. She hardly dared to hope that the Society on its side would accept so worthless a person as herself. She rose. Garden path, flower-beds, green grass plots, an oak door that opened into the cool dimness of the cloister. Miss Stuart passed through, and sought out one of the nuns.

"May I see Reverend Mother, please?"

In deep humility Mother Digby went down to the parlor. God was putting a treasure into her keeping. Hers to make it yield a hundredfold.

On September 7th, 1882, the new postulant arrived. Mother Digby's welcome, strong and tender, penetrated to depths beyond the outward reserve of Sister Stuart. Together they knelt before the altar of the Sacred Heart and made their offering to the Hidden God in the tabernacle. God first served: but the two souls who belonged so utterly to Him, He willed to bring together. His bonds were sure and safe.

"Reverend Mother, what makes us saints?" a novice asked at recreation.

"I think it is the direction of our thoughts," she answered reflectively. "We are not really here where our bodies are. Where our thought is, there is our love . . . there we are truly."

"My thoughts run about such a lot," sighed another novice. "If I could spend longer in the chapel instead of going to the scullery and then to the school and then to sweeping the corridor!"

"No," said Mother Digby. "The circumstances of our life matter little. If we are resolved to become saints, we shall fulfill that resolution, whatever the circumstances are."

"I don't seem to get anywhere," another put in. "I don't seem to have made any progress for weeks."

"Do you always expect God to pay you in ready money?" asked Mother Digby. "Give and work, because the Lord hath need of it; don't look only at 'the good day's wage for a good day's work!' And when you are traveling, live always in an express train which passes by the small stations. What do you think, Sister Stuart?"

Sister Stuart was silent. Her answer was not yet sufficiently thought out to be thrown into the midst of these novices who moved so easily among spiritual ideas. As she hesitated, someone broke in. The moment for speaking had passed.

She found Mother Digby waiting for her outside the room at the end of recreation.

"Do you feel as if God's air would never breathe on you again?"

"Yes," said Sister Stuart, and looked up into kind blue eyes that spoke more than the lips. Hope was born again in her heart. Somehow things would come right. Perhaps she would not be a fraud, unable to do anything. At least Reverend Mother Digby understood.

There were outdoor recreations, when they followed her with habits tucked up ready for any work that might come their way. The builders at work on the new buildings found precious allies in the "ladies in white" who followed the superior, and in very short time cleared the way for their labors. Mother Digby seemed to have eyes for everything. A drain was choked with dead leaves and mud. She bent down with them to clear the course, scooping out slime and débris with her hands. A quick glance up: a novice standing on the outside edge of the busy group; a word, quiet and penetrating, from Mother Digby: "Those white hands have not been given to Our Lord."

She led them by the end of the Chapel. Tall ladders left by workmen doing repairs leant against the gray stone bell tower.

"Sister Stuart, go up those ladders to the bell turret, and see how the world looks from there."

She watched her with a companion unhesitatingly obey her. She watched, too, how one or two on the ground murmured in relief that they had not been asked. She would have to lead them to other ladders than wooden ones if they were to climb the heights. Up aloft, Sister Stuart would be seeing the buildings at Roehampton dwarfed and compacted, the grounds set not in unlimited expanse but in the midst of other houses and gardens, and the novices and their mistress more midget-like beneath them. Would she make that view fit into the wider scheme of things that religious life would be showing her, and realize how small and impotent people became if they looked at things only from the human side? She had already a deep insight into obedience. The submistress of novices must be told to word orders to her very carefully, as she would carry them out to the letter. She had understood fully Christ's words "He that heareth you, heareth Me." What comfort to find such a novice!

Mother Digby was in her room, seeing novices who wished to come to her with their problems and joys, opening to her reverent gaze the innermost thoughts of their hearts. "Our life is truly a sanctuary," she reflected. "We are mysteries, each to each." God alone knew all. He entrusted some knowledge to others whom He meant to use as instruments. They must keep close to Him in prayer.

A tearful postulant came in. Mother Digby's kindness seemed to enfold her and she smiled through her tears.

"It is for your mother that I feel the separation," she heard her say. So this was not a cold piece of machinery producing religious for useful work; this was someone who felt for those left outside in the world. The postulant's words tumbled out. There was the house, the garden, the old dog, the swing that had been part of childhood's joys, the family meal, the mother who had already given five of her children to God . . . telling Reverend Mother Digby all this lightened the load. At the end the deepest thought came out.

"You want to do something great to prove your love for Our Lord?" asked Mother Digby. "Then begin straight away by offering what is hardest, most painful and most humiliating in the details of your life." A stern program? The only one to give the daughter of such a mother.

A novice brought her a tale of discouragement. Prayer was uninteresting, obedience oppressive, everything she did was going wrong, she did not feel the happiness and fervor of her first year in the noviceship. She felt all out of gear.

Mother Digby spoke to her of a life based on faith and its certainties.

"Principles alone remain and serve us as umbrella and waterproof in showers and storms. Feelings don't do that . . . but don't put up an umbrella between you and God in bad weather."

"What shall I do, Reverend Mother, then?"

"Go towards what is austere and what lowers us in the eyes of others."

The novice winced. How could she answer that? She remained silent. Quietly Mother Digby said, "Don't you want to be faithful to Our Lord?"

"Yes."

That was just the reality. The novice rose and went out. Prayer, obedience, success, failure: just tokens of her desire to be faithful to Christ.

The next novice came to report with satisfaction the work accomplished under her direction in the linen room. It was a pity that some of those who worked with her seemed at times grudging in answering her demands. She did her best, but they surely ought to have learned how to obey by this time. No. She did not always remember that authority made you the servant of others. No. She hadn't always time to be careful of charity when she worded her commands. Yes. Perhaps they should be requests.

"Yes, Reverend Mother, I know you've told me of that fault to correct before today. But I can't. I haven't the strength."

"Go to the infirmary, and ask for a tonic," said Reverend Mother Digby, gravely. That was final.

A remorseful face appeared at the door. The novice tremblingly brought from behind her back the scorched remains of a red embroidered cross.

"It's the cross for the chasuble you gave me to iron," she said. "It must have taken you hours and hours to embroider, and I've used an iron that was much too hot on it . . . and look what it's like now."

Mother Digby took the shreds of satin from her, brown and charred, and tossed them into the wastepaper basket with never a glance.

"My dear child," she said, "don't take it so to heart. God

wasn't in the least offended by your ignorance of the way to iron." That was all. At recreations later, the novices watched her fingers going swiftly to and fro on another embroidered cross. The chasuble was completed in time.

Sister Stuart came in. "You must take your part in recreation, Sister," said Mother Digby. "I have told you before that you must talk. Shyness is not an apostolic virtue. I don't expect to have to open this subject to you again. You must be thoroughbred in everything."

"Yes, Reverend Mother," said Sister Stuart.

"You must drop all the corporal penances Father Gallwey allowed you before you entered. You are not able to do that."

"Yes, Reverend Mother."

"You must go to the infirmary for a special drink after meals."

"Yes, Reverend Mother."

There was a slight clouding of the eyes that looked into hers. Mother Digby saw the obedient will crossed by the enquiring mind. The spirit was chafing under a restraint that seemed to pitch sanctity at a lower level.

"Why do you take more care of my body than of my soul, Reverend Mother?"

"You may have another Superior who can do for your soul what I have left undone, but if I let you damage your body, it can't be repaired."

There was no further questioning. As Sister Stuart went out, she was thinking, "I could do anything at her word. She never admits that an opportunity has been missed. I trust her."

Mother Digby was reflecting, "I have not made a mistake. Sister Stuart longs for common life as a fish for water. It is perfectly safe to take her from it for special work. She can be errand-boy for Mother Kerr. It will be good for her to see how a soul meets death, and she will understand how to help

Mother Kerr." God was good to let her join these two daughters of hers in whom He took delight, like ships that hail each other as one enters the harbor that the other is preparing to leave.

She listened to the ambitious program of another novice. It did not quite square with her day-to-day behavior. Mother Digby smiled.

"You are your own heroine, my child, but the heroism is completely lacking."

The novice opened her mouth to protest. Then the truth of the judgment struck her, and she burst out laughing. Together they relished the situation, and the novice's heart warmed more to her Mistress.

"Well?"

"Well, ought I to love people when I'm trying to love God?" Was it more laughter or deepest seriousness in those eyes that seemed to read her soul?

"We must purify the affections of the soul, my child, not kill them. God does not wish to be served by corpses." Of course things were right when Reverend Mother Digby put them in the right way. And she understood such silly little unworthy things. Even now she seemed to be excusing a fault owned up to.

"Reverend Mother, how can you understand such meanness?"

"From my own heart, my child."

How they missed her if she was away on visits to her other houses, or ill! She came back to them as soon as she could, meeting them during convalescence in a bath-chair and insisting on going to all parts of the garden.

"But, Reverend Mother, you aren't going to let the chair run down that slope with you!" cried a fearful novice.

"Sit down at my feet," said Mother Digby with a laugh. "Now someone give us a push and it will run with its own propulsion. I will steer." The chair gathered speed as it careered down the winding path. Mother Digby guided it round the curves. Memories of a baby boy crying with delight came back to her. She sensed the discomfort of the novice, whose weight sent them forward more quickly. They had left behind the other novices, running with them. Ahead there was a corner too sharp to be taken without upset. Very well then, she would not attempt it. Holding the steeringwheel steadily, she let the chair jump the low grass verge, career across the lawn and come to rest in the restraining masses of rhododendrons and peonies. The novice at her feet was laughing now. It was worth while to watch the alarmed faces of the others as they ran up, worth while, too, to have given them a further experience.

They learned much more from her explanations of the Rule and from the times when she spoke to them of God and His Goodness. Explaining the Rule, she could say that God was all and everything else nothing, but, living with her, they knew that this was so in her life.

"We must make a throne for God in our hearts," she said, "and go there often to adore."

They must learn to value silence.

"Be as miserly over your words as a miser is over his money. As soon as you have understood what religious life is, you will go out after silence. The mind may be filled with useless furniture, with scruples that deform, with dreams that distract and enervate. But the visit of God drives out all this lumber and makes the imagination fit to reflect the calm and serene images of eternity. And silence consecrates our difficulties . . . our silence is like a chalice, a ciborium which we give to God."

In the chapel she wrapped the novices about with her prayer, these souls so distinct and individual. No room here for smug complacency in a training well expressed and well ordered. There was always the individual's response to grace. Those two who had entered the chapel half an hour ago, and had knelt still, facing the Blessed Sacrament, He alone knew if one had been plunged into the ravishing depths of the Godhead, or the other given Him a beggarly five minutes of real prayer. Strong and supernatural: if she was to engender such religious for the Sacred Heart, she must be in travail for them in her prayer and in her life. She thought "I must let them see in reality that I am going on to God; they will come along with me if they will, but I myself must go on to God! . . . must catch at every stick or straw that will help me. . . . I must go on."

Chapter Twenty-five

1894

T H E pile of neatly folded mending grew steadily beside Sister Fanny Richardson. Through the open window the hot, still air of Paris entered unfreshened by the brown grass and motionless trees of the Mother House garden. There would be greenness even now about the lawns at Roehampton, and ducks stirring cool ripples in the lake. It would be good to be back there again, after this long month of the General Council, though life in the Mother House had been packed with interest, with all the Mothers Vicar from the whole world there to elect the new Mother General. They had chosen Reverend Mother de Sartorius, who had been Reverend

Mother Lehon's quiet aid as one of the four Assistants General. To Sister Richardson's practiced eye, she did not look very strong to support all the labor entailed, but you never could tell where holiness held a prescriptive claim to God's help. Now the Council had finished all its business, except for the election, this 12th day of August, of the Assistant General to fill the empty place.

The packing of the superior vicars' luggage was complete; soon she and Reverend Mother Digby would be crossing the Channel again, and there would be the drive up the Lane and all the Mothers and Sisters waiting at the door to welcome them back, and she would go up to her Infirmary and visit her invalids and tell them of all the happy and good things she had experienced at the center of the Society.

What work Mother Digby had accomplished in the years of her rule at Roehampton! The house at Wandsworth, with its flourishing Training College, its day school now, as well as its poor school, and its workroom for young girls; Brighton developing from its early house on the seafront, and its little boys as well as girls, into a large boarding school; the house in Dublin fulfilling for Ireland the frustrated Dorset Street plans; Carlisle, set in the midst of bigoted opposition in 1890, the Protestant minister and his friend visiting with a carpenter all their furnaces and trapdoors in search of walled-up nuns, while Bishop Wilkinson of Hexham and Newcastle cheered Reverend Mother Digby by his understanding of their chief function when he asked them to be "souls of prayer" in his diocese; and lastly God's ideas coming full circle when Archbishop Manning's successor asked to take over the buildings of the Seminary in Hammersmith for poor school, day school, meeting-place for the Children of Mary and center of parish congregations.

What fun they had had with Reverend Mother Digby, preparing the neglected place for instant occupation! Sister

Richardson thought of their arrival in the early morning at what the neighborhood was calling "Pope's Corner," of the crowd that gathered to watch them with their blue working aprons dismount from the brake with all their goods and chattels to carry in, of the sympathetic murmurs, "Poor dears, they're going in never to come out again!" If people did but know! If they could even a few hours later have glimpsed them all sitting round the one and only kitchen table with Reverend Mother Digby at their head, enjoying a picnic after their sweeping and washing and polishing!

Then there had been the nuns sent off from time to time to the foundations in Australia. She had been too young a religious in 1881 to realize what it must have cost to part with Mother Vercruysse, a fellow laborer at Marmoutier and in England, and how dedication to the interests of God exacted an aloneness with Him that could not rightly be called loneliness. How many other friends had been taken from Reverend Mother in these last years: Dr. Philip Harper, who, mortally ill, had risen to go to the bed of a dying woman; Mother Henrietta Kerr, never more to be her "jester" and to send her laughter ringing out at recreations; Mrs. Digby, upright and dignified to the end of her eighty-four years, humble and tender before God; Lady Georgiana Fullerton, her tale of hidden good works complete; and nuns whom she had loved with a mother's love, young and old, moving with them to the threshold of heaven. And yet how full the years had been of joyful things too, homely, unchronicled things, children laughing over their favorite game of cricket in the meadow, summer evening recreations beneath the great plane tree, Reverend Mother Digby provoking Mother Stuart to enlarge her thought, while the sunset's glory faded behind the Calvary and a benighted butterfly moved ghostlike above the glimmering flowers of the terrace . . . Christmas communion in the chapel the novices had brightened with berried holly from

167

the garden . . . the October day last year when the news came that the body of their saintly foundress had been found incorrupt . . . those heavenly days when she had been in Rome with Reverend Mother and had knelt with her to offer the Society's congratulations to Leo XIII for his Golden Jubilee and had seen the love he felt towards them, nuns and children, so lovingly loyal to him in his troubles. Heavenly days, yes, but they had been possible for her only through suffering. Perhaps that was the law of life; she had gone because Reverend Mother Lehon wanted Reverend Mother Digby properly looked after.

Sister Richardson remembered the anguish of the April of 1890, when peritonitis brought her to death's door, when for days she hung between life and death . . . when she had said with a flash of her true vigor, "You keep praying for my body, but not for my soul!" . . . and the Mother Assistant had said, "Yes, but it's important to keep them together." She had played her part in keeping them together . . . she, Sister Richardson, making use of all the skill Reverend Mother herself had taught her and now, whenever she had to travel, they sent her as well . . . A bell rang. She folded the pair of stockings she had mended, and rose. The meeting of the Mothers Vicar would be over, the fourth Assistant General elected. There would be the Magnificat to sing in the chapel, then nothing between Reverend Mother Digby and herself and home. She rose and went downstairs.

Mother Desoudin, Assistant General for more years than she liked to count, hobbling round on a stick, watched with bright, sharp eyes that belied her eighty-three years. There were smiles on all faces as the community gathered in the chapel . . . all faces except the English Sister's. That quiet smile that had made a child say that Sister Richardson made her think of the Blessed Virgin had vanished, and tears bathed the face she hid in her hands. The stall of the new Fourth

Assistant General was empty. She had seen Mother Digby slip alone into the little tribune of Our Lady of Perpetual Succour. There would be tears there, too, to be hidden from all eyes. At fifty-nine the burden to be borne had a longer future than at eighty-three.

Mother Desoudin caught Sister Richardson. She was getting ready to travel back to Roehampton alone.

"Don't cry, Sister, you'll come back."

Back? Was she really needed by Reverend Mother Digby? That would be a softening of the sacrifice of a loved way of life, the passing of an era and an order too happy to be permanent in this world.

Mother Desoudin looked shrewdly at Reverend Mother Digby when they met that night. She knew from her own remembered pain the suffering in the deep-blue eyes that looked back at her.

"At ten, tonight, when you are alone, you will cry a little, won't you?" she said softly. There must be pain, and from the pain the happiness of other souls was born. But God was tender and He had shed tears in the Garden of Gethsemane.

There was business to be done in Mother Digby's new position. Mother de Sartorius had chosen Mother Stuart to be Superior Vicar in her place in England. Mother Stuart, her "second self." That was better than her own continuing in office. All would be well with the work she had had in her heart these twenty-two years. On the Feast of the Presentation, she thought of the offering of the tiny child who was to be Mother of God, and of all that had flowed from that offering. What would she offer to her? The answer was not hard to find. She laid down Roehampton as a carpet for her feet on the steps leading to the Temple. Now she belonged wholly to the Mother House, to live and die for all the Society.

IV · Alleluia!
1895-1911

Chapter Twenty-six

1895

MATHIEU had grown old in the service of the Mother House. He knew a thing or two about its affairs, and watched its latest recruits with a critical eye. Reverend Mother Barat was the one for him; you couldn't catch her out in charity or in humility. . . . The young ones? Well, there was the standard set for them. No doubt it took some living up to. But he'd seen it maintained in the other Mothers General who had followed her. Three he'd known now. Reverend Mother Goetz, Reverend Mother Lehon, Reverend Mother de Sartorius, and now he'd be seeing a fourth.

Queer that God had taken Reverend Mother de Sartorius less than a year after they'd all met here to put her in her place at the head of the Society. And now here they all were again to find her successor. He had his ideas about who she should be. Yes. Humble and kind, like Reverend Mother Barat. He wondered how long the Mothers Assistants General and the Mothers Vicar would be in making up their minds. Cardinal Richard had said the Mass for them, and now they were all in the probation room. Nine o'clock it was when he'd watched them all file in. A good day for them to be choosing, the Feast of St. Louis of France and the Feast of the Immaculate Heart of Mary.

It looked as if St. Louis would be kept busy over the affairs of France, with the Anti-clericals in power and the bills they were bringing forward to tax the Religious Congregations. They'd go on trying to oust them by fair means or foul . . . had their knife into the teaching orders worst . . . take away the faith of the children and the next generation was theirs. A good job there were people who didn't mind a fight. They'd not get round Reverend Mother Digby, for example, for all she was kind and putting herself out for you. He'd watched her looking at the horses in the garden; she'd a way with them, know horses, know people. You wanted a firm wrist for some of both.

He thought of the hard times and the re-awakening of faith that followed. Over there on the hill of Montmartre the church of the Sacred Heart showed white against the blue August sky, reminding France of her need for reparation. He'd watched it rise these last two decades; it was good to call in when he was passing. Reverend Mother Barat had taught him how to pray to Jesus, Meek and Humble of Heart . . . that's what she was, that's what her successor would have to be.

The clock chimed the quarter. Mathieu roused himself from his meditations. The door of the Probation Room was opening. The Reverend Mothers were filing out and making for the chapel. A loud triumphant whisper burst from the old man's lips: "It's her!"

Mother Digby was taking her place in the empty stall of the Mother General.

Te Deum and rejoicing, gladness at the thought that all but one voting paper had borne her name, and that one in her own handwriting, happiness to see so well-loved a figure taking up the government under the protection of the Immaculate Heart of Mary, smiles and fervent thanksgiving, the words of the aged Cardinal ringing out: "The spirit of God reigns in your Society . . . you are governed by the Heart of Jesus, by Whom God has been pleased to manifest His love in our times . . .", certainty that His love had given them again a Mother. The Chapel of the Mother House was but the forerunner of the joy that was to spread throughout all the houses in the world. Upright on her prie-dieu, with eyes fixed on the tabernacle, Reverend Mother Digby felt the burden of motherhood of nearly seven thousand souls. How often had it been sweet to do the Will of God; how difficult today to accept it!

They waited for her in the Community Room. There was the chair set ready behind the little table. A saint had sat there, the saint who had spoken to her so lovingly of God; Reverend Mother Goetz, who had opened the way of religious perfection to her and shown her that truth and humility were one; Reverend Mother Lehon, so valiant in the service of God; Reverend Mother de Sartorius, so delicately sensitive to the least imperfection. Profanation for Mabel Digby to sit where they had sat, knowing that the Society had sunk to such a level as her. She had said just now to the Cardinal that she could not understand their choice of her, she was so utterly nothing. He had answered, "It's God's habit to choose a mere nothing to do His work!" That being so, there was one course alone open to her: she went forward to the chair that awaited her. Like Father de la Colombière, she would say: Jesus Christ can do very little if He cannot uphold me from day to day.

The Mother General's desk had plenty of letters to occupy her. There were business letters to send off to finish the purchase of the House at Aberdeen which Mother de Sartorius had authorized just before she died. Mother Digby had gone north—was it only last year?—with Mother Stuart and had after fruitless search seen a house that would be suitable enough though it was not then for sale. Perhaps Mother Henrietta Kerr's prayers had removed the obstacles after all these years of longing for Scotland. She would not see it now.

There was a letter to write to Roehampton: "Tell them to live and to love and to suffer for the glory of the Sacred Heart, in and through our Society; and never let anyone come down to a thought of self, which would be utterly low." There was a long letter to read dated Evreux, 27th of August. She turned to the signature: Bernard Perez, Man of Letters. He had seen her nomination in the newspapers. He had always meant to thank her, but time had slipped by, and only now was he paying "this debt of the heart." What gay memories he had carried away with his two legs from Marmoutier! As she followed his memories, she saw again the dimly lit wards, the men looking to her as great babies to their mother, the Mothers who had helped her, the chaplain . . . yes, like Bernard Perez, she found those memories gay.

She turned to the solicitor's letter, outlining the legal position of the French houses in respect of the Ribot-Brisson law of 1880, and read through the mounting sum of taxation that unpaid arrears were producing. It was harder to be gay in face of cold iniquity that tried to put a legal color on spoliation, whose only object was the killing of the teaching orders. But the Society would live as long as it was one heart and one soul in the Heart of Jesus. Persecution would draw the bonds of union the more close. She must go and visit the houses of Europe and of America, to put them in closer contact with the center.

Mother Desoudin and the Council of the Mother House were alarmed at the thought of America. The doctors had said her health was poor and her heart in a bad condition. Perhaps a journey to Rome might not come amiss since the Holy Father had asked to see her. The doctors even suggested that to winter in Italy might be a good thing.

Chapter Twenty-seven

1895

ON September 5th Mother Digby went to Conflans and, in the words that had come from the anguished heart of Madeleine Sophie Barat in 1839, when storm clouds darkened the sky and the very life of her little Society was endangered, she rededicated that Society to the Mother of Sorrows: ". . . Love gave thee the Cross," she read in her low melodious voice, "grant that the Cross may give us love and may the spouses of the Sacred Heart never know any cross but that of thy Son. May we bear about in ourselves the Cross of Christ, the sufferings of His Passion, and the remembrance of His Wounds. Grant that, wounded and bruised and following in His footsteps, we may be lifted above ourselves and consumed with the love of the Cross."

Mother Desoudin sighed, remembering how Mother Lehon had said, "Reverend Mother Digby likes suffering as others like sugar." Yes, she had understood the need for reparation, and a share in the Passion of Christ, like St. Paul, making up in her person what was wanting in His sufferings. Even as she sighed, she heard the Mother General's laughter breaking out, gay and witty, as she teased Mother de Pichon at recreation. Yes, a soul full of faith had the key to happiness. And her heart had been strengthened by the permission just granted for the Mother House to have daily Exposition of the

Blessed Sacrament in perpetuity. Watching her still absorption in the chapel, Mother Desoudin understood how she could face so much, even the hard criticism of friends and those in high places, with an unshaken calm.

By the end of October Mother Digby was journeying Romewards with Mother de Pichon and her secretary, Mother Le Baïl. Winter had set in, bleak and hard, and the French countryside was withdrawing into itself as though to conserve the last warmth of summer. Bleakness was falling on the religious orders whose houses were coveted by the government. Warmth could come from the center where the Heart of Jesus burned with love for men. She planned to see as many of her daughters as she could.

They reached Chambéry at night. In the greater silence, she went to the chapel to greet Christ in the Blessed Sacrament. As the heavy door swung open, the dark shadows retreated behind her. On each stall, in place of the nun who would have welcomed her in the brightness of the day, burned the steady flame of a candle. So, she prayed, would the brightness of their lives greet her when the night of persecution closed in on them. At Turin, they went out to Avigliana. In the quiet of its woods, beside the rushing river, with the mountains rising rampart-like, she tasted peace and joy.

"There are happy moments when I can forget I am Mother General," she said, and the laughter at recreation times spread around that happiness.

Padua, Florence, then Rome. On the 16th of November she was summoned to an audience with Leo XIII. Frail with age, the body illumined by spirit, the Pope spoke to her of the troubles of the time, cheering her and blessing her Society as a "chosen portion of the Church of God."

She went to see Father Martin, General of the Jesuits, asking how she could repay some parcel of the debt of gratitude towards his sons.

"Pray, and get others to pray that I may be humiliated and despised for the love of Our Lord," he said. He spoke to her, too, of the burden of governing others.

"Many people think you have to do it through the intelligence, by using your head. No! No! You will never govern perfectly or succeed in obtaining real good in all things except by suffering." Weariness of body was a form of suffering.

Mother Digby left Rome for Naples and the house of Portici on the vine-covered slopes of Vesuvius overlooking the great sweep of the bay. She laughed at their efforts on the journey to keep their attention on their usual spiritual exercises.

"It's quite useless for us to renew our resolutions not to look at all these beautiful things," she said. "These wonderful sights don't keep to an appointed time to show themselves and keep on interrupting in order to be admired."

Rome again, then on to Venice, where the Patriarch Cardinal Sarto was anxious for a foundation. As they journeyed along the smiling Adriatic coast, they remembered how, close on a hundred years before, Madeleine Sophie Barat, the decree for whose canonization they had just read posted up on the walls of the Vatican, had traveled this same way and had sent little pebbles skimming over the blue waves to those far shores where Agamemnon and Achilles, Hector and Ulysses, had shown her the stature of heroism.

Cardinal Sarto's gondola awaited the nuns, and swept them through the still waters of the canals to the Patriarch's palace. He made them sit at his table for dinner, the homely table presided over by his two sisters, and where any passing visitor could take an extra place. He took them by his private door into the basilica of St. Mark, then accompanied them to the house that was being offered them, pleased that it included a garden, since he was asking for an enclosed order of nuns to take charge of the children of his city.

From Venice they went on to Marseilles, at the turn of the

year. At each stop, Mother Digby gave herself without stint to the needs of the nuns. Mother de Pichon and Mother Le Baïl watched with anxiety, seeing how tired she was growing. Avignon, Aix. Then came news that Reverend Mother Desoudin was not well. Immediately Reverend Mother Digby took train for Paris, and stayed until the invalid's crisis was safely over. Then she took the train back to the visitation of the houses which had been disappointed. Montpellier, Perpignan, Toulouse, Pau, passing by the grotto of Massabielle, where the child who had been the same age as Eva had seen the Immaculate and now had called thousands to fresh love of God. Layrac, Bordeaux, Angoulême. There remained Poitiers. The bitter winter was breaking at last, and a spring-like warmth was in the night air as in the dark they drove up to the old house of the Feuillants. Time disappeared. Here was the house where Madeleine Sophie Barat trained the first novices of her Society, praying and suffering for them that they should mirror the beauties that God was showing her, that they should become books in which all could read something of the love of God in the Heart of His Son. Dim lights led the way to the open door. Only Reverend Mother du Chélas was there with a few mothers to greet the travelers. In the chapel the organist was playing softly the Magnificat. She was entering the chapel entered so often before by her holy predecessor. She was responsible for seeing that what the foundress had envisaged should be carried on in succeeding generations. She would ask that the prayer of this house should always be that the primitive spirit of the Society should never fail.

The next day she saw the children. "Children," she said, "understand the Mass and love it. I will meet you always there."

To the nuns she said, "Religious life is suffering chosen and embraced by love. This share in suffering we ask each day in the Mass, when we pray to have a part with the apostles and martyrs. Isn't that asking for suffering—and no light suffering at that . . . but the words that follow give us the secret of the strength to fulfill it. By Him, and with Him, and in Him . . . the secret not of strength alone, but also of joy."

The Reverend Mothers consulted together. The Mother General was quite clearly keeping on by will alone. The doctor was called in. He did not wrap up the truth.

"In rising from her chair or in stooping to pick up anything, she runs the risk of dropping down dead."

Mother Digby listened unmoved and returned according to schedule to Paris. In great alarm at her condition, Mother Desoudin sent a letter round to all the houses of the Society, begging for prayers. The doctors thought it probable that she could last three or four weeks, scarcely more. As answering letters returned, Mother Digby was surprised. She must, then, be ill indeed. And America? What of America? Again time closed in. She was kneeling beside Reverend Mother Barat, the tired kind eyes searching hers, the assured voice. America, the sign of her father's salvation.

Mother Desoudin came to her, her old face drawn and anxious.

"Reverend Mother, you must come to the chapel with me." There before the Blessed Sacrament, lifting up her heart to the first Mother General, while she held the hand of the fifth, she said, "Promise that if you get back enough strength, you will go to America." It was her challenge to God, as it were. He should have what she had always opposed. Reverend Mother Digby smiled and promised.

By June she had recovered enough to continue her ordinary work, but Mother Desoudin in the fullness of age and good works, had gone to God on the Feast of the Sacred Heart.

There was plenty to do in the summer of 1896. With the Econome General, Mother Borget, Mother Digby examined the position of the French houses in the eyes of the law, and planned for their safety in any event. With the coming of winter, the doctors insisted that she should go to the warmer climate of Rome and return only with the spring.

"It costs me much," she said, "to leave the Mother House for so long, and to cause an expense to the Society when my only wish is to render it all the service in my power."

She gave herself to the Roman houses, the Trinità dei Monti, Santa Rufina and the Villa Lante. The work of the whole Society was carried on with its increasing difficulties. As spring approached, she planned to return to France by way of the Austrian houses. Preparations were made, and the day of departure fixed. Then on March 27th, a sudden heart attack seized her. The doctor came in haste and asked that the priest should be at hand. She lay with eyes closed, the heart scarcely beating, propped up in a chair while the nuns around her prayed in agony. Suddenly, as if waking from sleep, she opened her eyes. She saw the anxious faces bent over her, the doctor beside her, and a smile passed over her face. "I am not for San Lorenzo's this time," she murmured.

The doctor gave his directions. With care she might certainly rally. Perhaps the Last Sacraments were not needed today. In any case she could receive the Blessed Sacrament as viaticum the following morning.

"We can do no more," said Mother Le Baïl the next day. "Thank God she has been spared this time again."

"Mother!"

Mother Digby was calling her. She was looking curiously at her secretary.

"Mother, I hope you have everything packed. We shall leave the day after tomorrow for Austria."

Mother Le Baïl opened her mouth to speak, but words failed her. "The day after tomorrow, Reverend Mother?" Mother Digby was laughing at her consternation.

"The doctor thinks I may die any moment in my armchair. I shan't run any greater risk in the train."

There was nothing more to be said. Two days later she set off for the station, boarded the train and traveled to Vienna. The journey was long. There was no opportunity of praying before the Blessed Sacrament.

"Who travels much, rarely becomes holy," she sighed. "But Gods wants me to become a pilgrim. That is enough."

Budapest, Prague, Pressbaum, all the houses of the Austrian Vicariate seen and warmed by her presence, then the Mother House at Paris again for the summer: autumn with a fresh round of houses to be visited before Rome was reached. Algiers, the Spanish houses as well as all those of France; an audience with the Holy Father; a sudden question: "Does Your Holiness approve of my visiting America?" Leo XIII's startled answer: "You must ask the doctors. Won't it put your life in danger?" A quick murmured reply, "The Society won't lose much." Darkening skies over France . . . still more houses to visit . . . two years passing by and a promise still unfulfilled. All things safely in the hands of God to be shaped as He willed.

Chapter Twenty-eight

1898

MOTHER DIGBY'S embroidery needle went to and fro as she listened to the visiting Superior.

"We really do need a harmonium to make the chapel

services worthy of God. Song makes such a difference, too, to the education of the children. I have made all kinds of enquiries and there is a little one that does not cost a great deal of money. I know my house is poor, but . . . would you sanction my buying it?"

The needle went slowly into the material, and was drawn out slowly. Then Mother Digby spoke.

"No, Reverend Mother, you will not buy that harmonium. . . . I will give it to you."

She cut short her visitor's thanks as Mother Le Baïl came in for letters. Mother Digby smiled.

"My hand and my memory . . . no one knows what Mother Le Baïl is for me! My only quarrel with her is that she thinks a long life better than a short one."

"Of course," retorted Mother Le Baïl. "The older I become, the more pleased I shall be . . . up to a hundred years and beyond, if it pleases God."

"And the longing to see Him?" asked Mother Digby.

"I feel it, but also I want to work and suffer for Him."

"But on certain days," persisted Mother Digby, "when the world gives you thorns?"

"There aren't any with you."

Mother Digby laughed. "Some call religious life a martyrdom . . . we shall all go to heaven with the instrument of our martyrdom. Mother Le Baïl will go with her pen."

Sister Richardson was waiting to slip into the room as they left.

"Reverend Mother, I have to write to the Sisters at Roehampton and I can't find anything to say. Have you any ideas?" they heard her ask as the door closed.

"What a Mother she is . . . and what a friend!" commented the visiting Superior. "I understand Mother Colgan saying, when she got her obedience for Australia, 'One would go through fire for Reverend Mother Digby.' "

Mother Le Baïl nodded. You could trust her not to alter with time. Her unchangeableness was the security of friendship.

From Number 11 of the rue de Mont Cénis that climbed to the sparkling basilica of Montmartre, another woman who trusted her friendship was coming. As she walked through the narrow streets and across the boulevards towards the rue de Varenne, Adèle Garnier was thinking of the time, nearly thirty years before, when she had spent two happy months as a postulant in the noviceship at Conflans, until the overwhelming happiness of belonging to the Sacred Heart had proved too much for her frail body; of the vision that had fallen on her and persisted with her for eighteen months, showing her a High Altar with the Blessed Sacrament exposed, while a voice said, "It is here that I wish you to be": of her message to the Archbishop of Paris that Christ's desire was that His Sacred Heart should be specially honored by Perpetual Adoration in the chapel at Montmartre; of the year of solitary life in the attic beside the chapel, and the nine years of illness at home that had followed. She felt the burden of her sixty years now would have been too great, had not God raised up friends to help her in this new work He had demanded. Now that Cardinal Richard had smiled on her project, not the least of her friends was Reverend Mother Digby. How generously she gave time and thought and encouragement to the working out of Constitutions for this new congregation! Adèle Garnier walked through the grounds of the Mother House of the Sacred Heart and was heartened by the thought of the welcome that awaited her from the Mother General. There was one who knew, as she herself knew, the treasures of the Eucharistic Heart of Christ.

Listening to Mlle. Garnier's plans, Mother Digby's memories were astir.

"We shall pray for the conversion of the country in which our houses are established."

Mother Cecil Kerr bursting into her room in those happy distant days of Marmoutier when she was a nobody . . . "I've been thinking that neither you nor I pray half enough for the conversion of England." . . . England, that the Martyrs had prayed for . . . her own ancestor, Henry Morse, giving his life at Tyburn . . . prayer to the Heart of Jesus . . . yes, she must give Mlle. Garnier every possible aid to establish prayer on this French Hill of Martyrs, for the conversion of France. Strange how, in times of danger, God raised up new workers. The Church was strengthened by persecution, even by the legal persecution of the anti-clerical laws.

It seemed to her, in the spring of 1898, that the storm in France was not yet breaking. She spoke to her Council about the fulfillment of Mother Desoudin's promise. They accepted her faith and agreed to her making arrangements for visiting the houses of America. It might be the last chance. On August 6th she left the Mother House with Mother Stuart, Sister Richardson and young Mother Gurdon. As the sound of the horses' hoofs died away, Mother Le Baïl turned to go to her room, wondering if she would ever see the beloved face again. But she was learning that real love lets others receive the love of the loved one. She was understanding a little more of Christ's Mother's love for Him in the long years of the Public Life.

The travelers crossed to England, and journeyed to Roehampton. There was an English cheer from the children who swarmed round the carriage as it drew up before the white house sleeping in the summer sun. Mother Digby walked round the well-known places. The great oak cast its shadows across the meadow, the copper beech was darkening to purple, there was a new family of moor-chicks a-sail on the lake, bright-eyed squirrels chattered at her from the trees and the pert robins came to watch her. How peaceful it all seemed and how distant the acrid atmosphere of French politics! But the sunny days could not be prolonged and on August 11th they were journeying north to Liverpool. The *Dominion* was berthed along the quayside. The harbor, with its tugs churning the water between the funneled liners and great cargo boats, only small-sailed vessels sliding between, seemed to belong to another world from that in which eighty years before the *Rebecca* had carried Mother Duchesne from Bordeaux to found the first house in the New World. How that valiant soul had longed that the first Mother General, Reverend Mother Barat, should visit the American foundations . . . now she was going there, the first Mother General to set foot in America. Ten weeks of buffeting by winds and waves had been their lot in 1818: ten days only lay between Liverpool and Montreal in 1898.

They ran into rough weather in the first part of the voyage, but, as they neared their destination, the sun shone and the sea grew calm. Spouting whales and the refracted light on gleaming icebergs were matters of delight, but the wonders of the deep were only the prelude to those of the land.

On 20th August, Mother Digby set foot on the soil of the New World, with a joy that surprised her in its intensity. America . . . the sign of her father's happiness had been given. Did she need it now? Her certainty of the love of God and His Infinite Mercy lay deeper than any sign. As they drove from the quay with the sun sinking behind Montreal, and took their way through the shady woods, catching sight of the swift-flowing river, she knew that a great grace was given her . . . the grace of witnessing to the power of God expressed in the unity of minds and hearts in the Heart of His Son. The twinkling Chinese lanterns hung along the trees of the drive gave warning that the convent was near, and she stepped from the carriage into the midst of her daughters, as truly of the family as those she had left in Europe. Sault au Recollet was home as really as Paris.

Sister Richardson shook her head at the itinerary that lay before them. After the Sault, Montreal's city claimed the Mother General, and then Grosse Pointe, Halifax. Beside the calm blue waters of the lake, Paul Goreham, chief of the Mic Mac tribe, came with his wife Silver Sal, their child, the judge of the tribe and his wife to do honor to her. His waving feathers and his impassive face gave Sister Richardson food for thought.

"Don't go near him alone," she counseled softly, "he might still be a little savage."

Listening to his fine full voice as he sang the *Veni Creator* in his own language, Mother Digby was back in Sugar Creek with Mother Duchesne, feeling something of the heart-ache of the great missionary for the souls of her Red Indians. There were still nuns she would meet who had followed the fortunes of the Potawotamy tribe through thirty years. What were her own labors in face of the hardships they had undergone? How great was the faith of these American nuns who welcomed her with such joy and reverence, discerning in so vile an instrument as herself the authority of the Mother General. Even her English nuns, who should have known better, had sent a telegram to her on the *Dominion* on August 17th, remembering that it was the day she had first arrived at Roehampton. It had run, "Her children rose up and called her blessed." Weren't they fools to think thus of her? God knew her better . . . her place, the place she loved to be in, was among the little and the humble. She was loving all the meetings with the boarding school children and their parents and the Children of Mary, but best of all, the children of the Poor Schools, coming in their hundreds to be taught the truth of the love of God.

Seven hundred children met her at Chicago. It was hard

to tear herself away from the nuns here, but she had to teach them the lesson she herself was learning each day more and more: the peace of soul that came with union of will with God's Will in a great loving confidence, united each with all so that in the Heart of Jesus there were no separations.

Clifton, Cincinnati, spread its peaceful countryside before her. "I am afraid I shall be spending some time at my window," she said, but the train carried her away too soon to Missouri, and days and nights spent in jolting expresses added to her sum of tiredness. The nuns at Maryville heard her laughing remark, "Since in America everything goes at full speed, we must go at the same rate in the ways of perfection." She gave permission for the house to be lit with the new electric light. They would be the admiration of the neighborhood, but "Don't think of what the world will say; only of what God will say," she said. "And take always the straight path no matter what it costs you or what may come."

Mother Le Baïl's post came to her from the Mother House with careful regularity, keeping her in touch with all her business. She found time to add a personal note to her official replies to her secretary.

"If you knew how I miss my memory and my hand!" she wrote to her from St. Louis. "Pray for my arduous work. Yesterday was the thirty-fourth anniversary of my Profession and I have so much need to prepare myself for the great journey, the final meeting with my God . . . your God . . . your only Love. How far away we are, even for correspondence! May Our Lord and His Holy Mother bless you. May Our Lord watch over you. I miss you so much. My heart is one with yours and follows you in your work and solitude. Is it solitude, since I share it? There is none in Him who is our center and meeting-place. How I pray for you, my very dear child! I am hungry for news but I am content with all that our Good Master gives, sends and decides. In Him I am with you all the time. If you knew how I miss my hand and memory and my daughter's heart. Pray for me . . . while we are still waiting for heaven . . . let us be there in heart and mind."

It was like the antechamber of heaven to go to St. Charles on November 7th with a radiant autumn sun lighting up the burning colors of the trees, glorious against a blue sky. They took her to the tiny chapel and showed her the place where lay all that was mortal of Mother Duchesne.

"This is a holy place," she said with awe, "a sanctified place."

They showed her the little cell where the great Missionary had died, and she went there to spend long hours in prayer.

"Our Mother General must be cured here," said Mother Burke to Mother Stuart. The Scotswoman had her own prayer. Philippine Duchesne must use her power with God to gain for Mother Digby not alleviation but the daily bread of strength and suffering together. Within the tiny room Mother Duchesne was giving her own gift to the Mother General.

Here were the high thoughts of God from which none had the right to descend. An old chair, reseated with cord and strips of buffalo hide by the old nun herself, exercise books of old envelopes cut and sewn together, a poor table, two old statues too unfashionable to serve for anyone else, these spoke more eloquently than words of the poverty that each religious should regard as her mother. On the wall hung the picture of St. Francis Regis given in the early difficult days by Bishop Dubourg. Before the picture, how many ardent prayers had gone up for the souls of children of all nations, how many burning longings that the precious pearl entrusted to Madeleine Sophie Barat's little Society should sanctify the hands that held it, should be shown to all the world as the Sanctuary of the Godhead and the Tabernacle of the Most Holy Trinity, so that all the nations of the world would be renewed and reach their last end! There lay her Office book, old and worn with much singing of the praises of God. Mother Duchesne was teaching their need for adoration, for prostrating the soul before the Infinite Majesty, in silence and self-contempt, not letting frivolous familiarity spoil the child's true reverence for the Father, for remembering always the dignity of the Heart of Jesus, Victim of Love. There lay her crucifix, kissed how often by lips silent under suffering, contempt, misrepresentation and loneliness. It cried aloud the need for reparation, for making up to Christ for His insults and grief at the loss of souls, by generous sacrifice, work, suffering and penance. Beside the crucifix was her rosary, the beads shiny where the ageing fingers had traced the cycle of the mysteries of Christ's love, that love He had shown in deeds more than in words and which she had understood in her patient, penitent desire for all His interests, "running, flying, rejoicing" in His service since suffering itself was an expression of love. Adoration, reparation, love, how their own petty lives would take on fuller stature, inheritors of all the promises made to Blessed Margaret Mary, as leaven in the world, working for its salvation! Philippine Duchesne was very near, her spirit speaking out from all these things she had used. Reverend Mother Digby sat down at her table, dipped her pen in the ink, and put on paper for all the Society the thoughts that filled her mind.

St. Joseph, Omaha, across the Sierra Nevada into California, San Francisco, Menlo Park, a warm December sun on palms and orange trees, rocky sandy wastes with giant cactus plants fantastic in their silhouettes, a day's wait for the one and only train at the Mexican frontier, Guadalajara at last after sleepless nights, children in their hundreds, nuns waiting for the maternal inspiration, a mule-drawn carriage journey to Guanajuato, among the quiet of mountains, three hundred members of an Indian congregation coming to be presented each separately, while the whole body repeated in chorus the verses of welcome sung by their leaders—these memories thronged in her mind as the train at length bore her on January 23 into the station of Grand Coteau.

"If these walls could speak!" said Mother Digby. "What precious holy memories they would bring back!" She looked over the fields as Mother Audé must have looked to see Mother Duchesne coming with Thérèse Pratt after their long journey down the Mississippi to help the struggling new foundation among the plantations. Mother Hardey, kindly Assistant General when she was a young nun, seemed to stand beside her, a golden-haired and curious girl summing up the holiness of the woman who cared nothing for wealth and ease. There were white-haired Old Children who came to meet her, who were young in the days of pioneering difficulties. Their children and their children's children loved Grand Coteau and showed their love to the visitor from Europe. The Congregations of colored girls and women waited under the pine trees, bright black eyes sparkling, bright-hued clothes throwing up the ebony of their faces, and read an address of welcome which ended in song, inviting her to remain for ever in their midst. The colored children crying out to her as she went along the road, scrambling around her to receive her gifts, the little boys and girls of the parish school all spick and span to welcome her; there was a timelessness about them that sent her thoughts straight into eternity, that great ever-present consideration that ruled all acts and judgments. In the woods, as she went round the property, they came upon a little well. It was as it had been when Mother Duchesne came, bucket in hand, to draw water for the community in the old white house. At any moment she might come down through the trees to help her draw waters from the Saviour's fountains. Mother Digby decided to make here her annual eight days' retreat. Silence closed down on her; only the happy

192

laughter of children at their play and the merry notes of birds came to her ears. Sister Richardson rejoiced that body as well as soul would be rested. St. Michael's already was preparing numberless receptions for her.

On February 9th she was on the road again and had reached this new house in the warm sunshine of Louisiana. The children proudly presented her with a ball of cotton in place of a bouquet, the Negro women came in crowds to the parlor to show her their babies and to claim knowledge of the early Mothers who had taught in the school. Then on the 12th, a great blizzard swept down on the country. Snow fell all night and froze over. The Mississippi filled with large sheets of ice, blocking the port of New Orleans. In the teeth of a bitter wind Mother Digby moved on to New Orleans, where torrential rain was washing away the snow. The nuns were down on their knees mopping up a flood of water when she arrived unexpectedly early. The roses of the garden had all been spoilt, the decorations planned were swamped. But she was in their midst, smiling and happy in spite of wind and rain. "It's always fine weather here," she said, kneeling before the altar in the chapel. "I come to see your souls, not your walls." But she looked at their walls, too, and gave money for the immediate building of a better school for the children of the parish.

Philadelphia, Eden Hall, Atlantic City, New York, with its two houses, Boston, Easter at Manhattanville, walls and souls calling for her attention. Albany-Kenwood at last on April 19th. There was important work here for her to accomplish. The young nuns of the country should in future meet all together for higher studies, according to the plan of the Society, and all the Noviceships of North America should be united.

"It's wonderful to think," commented Sister Richardson with a slip of paper in her hand, given her by an amateur statistician, "that our Mother has seen 35 houses, 1,728 nuns,

2,846 boarding school children, 4,732 parish school children, 2,954 Children of Mary, and some two thousand other people . . . and she's still alive."

On May 3rd, with Mother Stuart and Sister Richardson, Mother Digby went to Boston and boarded the liner that was to take them back to Liverpool. As the coast of America grew dim, her heart was warm with gratitude. In the New World she had touched a living truth, that her daughters were one heart and one mind; the prayer that had come from Christ's Heart at the Last Supper had been answered and they were all one, as the Father and the Son were one, and this sign the world would see and believe.

"Keep this will of their hearts," she prayed, and faced towards the Old World. She needed all the consolation that union could bring if she was to face the troubles that awaited her in Paris.

Chapter Twenty-nine

1900

A T ninety, life cannot hold many more years. Leo XIII saw a century growing old, distracted and troubled. Before he died, he would give it the one remedy for its ills that would restore courage and joy. He would consecrate the whole world to the Sacred Heart. At the opening of the next hundred years, all men had been placed in that safe sanctuary.

"Are you pleased, you nuns of the Sacred Heart?" he asked

Mother Digby when he saw her in Rome in the January of 1900. They had other cause for rejoicing, too, in this year of Jubilee which marked for them a century of existence. Since that day in the little secret chapel of the rue de Touraine, when Madeleine Sophie Barat had dedicated herself to the Sacred Heart, her Society had grown and labored and suffered, and always with entire devotion to the Holy See. On February 20th, he penned a letter of congratulations to "Our well-beloved daughter, Josephine Digby," joining in her thanksgiving for all the graces of a century, showing his affection and esteem, and hoping for fresh increase as a pledge of heaven's blessings.

In the Mother House, on November 21st, Mother Digby knelt in front of the selfsame picture before which the first vows of the Foundress had been made, and saw through the lights and the flowers that surrounded it the Mother and Child in each other's embrace, each showing the other to those who drew near, the warm brown tones of the painting homely as a hearth fire.

She had urged a preparation of three years of prayer for this great day, so that the nuns should reach it with all the maturity of age and the ardor of youth. Leo XIII had hymned the praise, honor and glory due to the Divine Heart: theirs to praise by the perfection of their Office, their liturgical worship, their perfect religious discipline, the whole loving movement of their souls towards God: to give glory with a zeal that could never cry "It is enough": to honor by lives made each day more perfect solely for His sake. Those who had gone before had shown the way to bring Him a multitude of souls formed on His model, so that the worship, love and glory of the Sacred Heart should spread throughout the world, souls of children, souls of the poor, that cherished portion of His flock, souls they had reached through retreats or personal contacts, and had weaned from sin or set on a more perfect life, souls they had gained for Him just by their prayer, unseen, unknown souls the fruit of the hidden prayer and suffering of those by age and sickness unable to be in touch with bodies. So much still to be done!

Kneeling here now, she thought of the hundred and forty-two houses spread over many countries. She thought of the forty-six French houses whose existence after so many years was at stake. They were all united, as their Foundress had hoped, the precious pearl of union she had bought with the blood of her heart. Now she was to receive the tribute of the Church's praise. Each day brought nearer the time of her beatification. Even as persecution came closer, her glory rose brighter, to be a comfort and a rallying-point for those who were to suffer in some measure as she had. A hundred years had seen the Society sowing in tears, knowing days of opposition, of persecution, darkness and perplexity. Yes, but also days of unspeakable joy when the chalice seemed overflowing with the sweetness of divine consolations, moments when Heaven reached down to earth. This day Christ was very near. His felt presence made it seem a little thing—no more than a passing dissonance in His triumphant cry, I have overcome the world!—that just beyond the Mother House grounds in the Chamber of Deputies, men were working out plans to speed up the spoliation of the religious orders begun by the Law of 1895.

Some religious had left the country already. On this very day, Adèle Garnier and her community were putting on the habit of their congregation for the first time in the house they had found in England, leaving the hill of Montmartre to find shelter near the hill of Tyburn. Mother Borget had shown her the demand for 1,000,000 francs made by the Government, and had said the State would sell by force one of their schools if they did not—as they could not—meet the taxation. On principle there could be no question of payment. Justice was to be maintained. How? She remembered Leo XIII's words: "You have made the decision not to yield, now you must trust to God." A century of trust lay behind them. The sure life of the future lay in fidelity to that oneness of heart and mind that was the central thought of their Foundress. What thoughts of the unknown future had filled her mind a hundred years before as she knelt here, and saw the eyes of the Mother and the Child looking out at her? She would have understood a great capacity for love, for suffering and for giving. She, Mabel Digby, most unworthy successor, would lay down here also at the feet of Christ, every personal view, every atom of self-love, to love God before and above all, to love others for Him, and especially to love those who were linked together by the close chains of spiritual relationship . . . one heart and one mind in His Heart. This glorious day of triumph would pass. After the glories of Palm Sunday came the shouts outside Pilate's palace. Well, they would carry on their work in the schools as long as they could. Those who asked to be admitted to the Society must be shown the hard way that lay before them. There must be no feeble or uncertain soul, none who might waver when the time of testing came. There was no place for sentimentality, only for the disciplined heart that loved deeply and strongly.

The early months of 1901 passed by in the ordinary round of school life in France. The summer term was drawing to its close when the first blow fell. On the 1st, the right of teaching was withdrawn from any congregation that had not received authorization. There was an ominous threat that associations with foreign administrators could be dissolved by decree. Mother Digby reviewed the authorizations of 1807, 1827 and 1853 and knew that some of the houses of later foundation were legally not covered by them. On the 5th she renewed the selfsame consecration to Our Lady of Sorrows that had been made on July 5th, 1839, by the woman whose heroic virtues were even now being recognized by the Church. The next day, the letter of Leo XIII to the heads of religious orders was delivered to her. She lingered long on his words: "There is a voice ever living and fraught with new courage, which reaches across the centuries: Have confidence, it says. I have overcome the world."

Confidence. She wrote to her own nuns: "I dare count on my daughters so that not one of them will yield to despondency. Children of our Venerable Mother, bound to the Heart of Jesus by our holy vows, we are also obliged to practice that courage and confidence which were our first watchword. Courage and confidence which are ours by right as long as we live under the strict observance of our Institute. If we are faithful to it, the Providence of God will have care of us, with all-powerful foresight."

She made application for authorization, envisaging at the same time the possibility of refusal. She began planning for the future in face of the uncertain present. In January 1902, the little house at Joigny, where Madeleine Sophie Barat had been born and had grown to womanhood, was handed over to the safe keeping of friends. Up and down France came the news of the violent expulsions of nuns of other orders from their convents. The Children of Mary banded themselves together in campaigns of prayer. In March 1903, they were all united in a novena to win the safety of the schools that had brought up themselves, their mothers and their grandmothers.

On March 21st, a friend called at the school of Belle Croix at Moulins and asked to see the Superior.

"They say a list has arrived today at the prefecture. It will give those houses for whom authorization has been refused."

"And if we are on the list?" asked Mother Mathieu.

"It will mean closure . . . but you can't be on the list . . . Moulins is the house nearest to Paray le Monial . . . nearest to Our Lord's Heart."

"Nearest to the thorns that crown it," thought the superior.

Friends came again on the next day. Children sensed there was something wrong. There were those who had seen the list at the prefecture. The school of the Sacred Heart headed it. Mother Mathieu waited for the official notification. The following day, the house was besieged by well-wishers come to sympathize. The prefecture was still silent. As the color left the sky behind the black March trees of the Avenue and the clock struck seven, slipping up to the door in the gathering dusk, the police agent handed in the official form. Mother Mathieu turned to the signature: Combes, Minister of the Interior and of Worship. She read: "I have decided there is no need to pass on your case to the Council of State in view of the authorization solicited. In consequence I have the honor to notify you that your request is refused." That was final enough. She read on, seeing that he was ordering her "to disperse and close your establishment within a month. I notify you that in case of the non-execution of this decision, you run the risk of imprisonment and fine." A month. Short enough notice to undo the work of half a century, but they could manage to save something from the ruin. She set to work to plan immediate action. The children must be put into safety first. The parents were informed and asked to come for the girls. They began straight away to pack for them.

The postman arrived the next morning with a letter from Mother Digby. The official notification had been delivered simultaneously at the Mother House, but with the addition of a shortening of the time of grace. If they were not out of Moulins within the week, action would be taken against them. In Belgium, the newly established house at Flône would receive children and some nuns. She indicated where others should go to receive another home. Wherever there was a house of the Society, they would find Our Lord waiting for them in the tabernacle. They would always be His.

Mother Mathieu was heartened. Quickly she reorganized their preparations to speed up their departure. Parents and friends came in crowds and refused to go away while there was any work to do. On the morning of March 25th, bright with the promise of the Annunciation, the children filed into the chapel in their white veils for the last Holy Communion. Thereafter the organ was silent, the chapel dismantled. Only the Blessed Sacrament remained. There were eight children who had come to be prepared for their First Holy Communion. With tears they begged that they might meet Christ before He and they were driven away into exile. The happy voices of children had gone from the house. Only the sound of hammer on wood, as packing-cases filled by the willing helpers were fastened down and the noise of heavy furniture being slid along corridors echoed in the house. There was no time to talk and fathers and mothers hard at work moved about as silent as monks. The eight, thrown close to the sufferings of Christ, grew wise with the understanding that comes from the cross. He came to them at the last Mass offered at the altar of Mater Admirabilis in the little chapel of the Children of Mary. From far and near Old Children gathered there, overflowing into the corridors, kneeling close together, hearts too wounded for tears. A last look, then the picture that had watched over their growing womanhood was taken down.

M. Delahaye had helped, day after day. Up and down stairs he had labored to carry the equipment of the school where his children had been happy and taught the things that mattered in life. He had superintended the packing of the last mattress his broad shoulders had brought down. Anger suddenly flared up and he ran into the room where Mother Mathieu was working.

"Reverend Mother," he cried, "this is iniquitous. It is nothing but robbery. There is not the slightest excuse for turning you out in this way. It is not I alone who speak;

there are many of us, fathers and husbands of your children, ready at your word to take arms in hand and defend you against expulsion in this way. We have fought for France, to keep her free and honorable . . . we are ready to fight again for the same reason. You have but to say yes."

Mother Mathieu shook her head. Each day she had had a letter from Mother Digby. She knew that she must follow her counsels; they were being called upon to share the lot of those who would live godly in this world. As the Master, so the servant. M. Delahaye, between tears and rage, knew that she was right. He went back to his task, turning aside the thanks of the nuns.

"Pray God for me and my children," he said. "That is all the thanks I want."

On March 29th the house was emptied. The first nuns to leave for Belgium and England went down to the station. A huge crowd had gathered to see them off, standing silent as they stepped into the carriage, which had been filled with flowers. Sullenly among them was a group of men who worked for the radical newspaper. One broke the silence nodding towards the nuns.

"I'd like to see a bomb knock off all those heads," he cried.

The train was moving slowly from the platform. The crowd broke into loud cries.

"Long live the Sacred Heart! Long live Jesus Christ! Long live Mother Barat! Long live our Mothers! Good-bye! We shall see you again!" Only Mother Mathieu remained now with four nuns in the ruins of her house. On March 31st a friend's carriage came to take them to the station. All the neighborhood was there in silent respect. A woman thrust a sheaf of white flowers into her hands.

"Your house has gone, Reverend Mother, but it lives in the memories of those who have so loved it. . . ."

Across the empty, deserted house, somcone was painting

the indictment: Stolen Property. In Paris, Mother Digby, before the tabernacle, offered Christ this first fruit of persecution.

Orleans, the two houses at Lyons, Le Mans, Pau, Layrac, Annonay and Nancy. One by one they were taken from her. Sydney, St. Joseph's, Missouri, Palma, Peschiera, Zybletowska Gora, Chorrillos. One by one she opened new houses. Two thousand six hundred religious who would be forced to leave France . . . Leamington, Malta, Cairo . . . there would be fresh homes for them . . . she pored over the map where one by one the lights before the tabernacles were being extinguished, and saw where workers were being needed in other fields, pondering over each religious to soften the blow by sending her where her aptitudes or age would be most at home.

"There are flowers in the garden of that house," she said, and named a nun who loved them to take a place there. Exile? No. They would find the love of Christ in His Society wherever they came to rest. And if there were some who would not be able to exercise their powers in lands where a language foreign to them was spoken, well, "You can always peel potatoes," Mother Borget had said, and prayer knew no boundaries of language.

"You should stay, Reverend Mother, here in France. Give up your religious habit, accept secularization, the government will license you and you will save education for the children you are teaching in France." It was a specious argument put to her time and again, sometimes by men in high authority. Yes, they would remain teachers, but they were first and foremost, in the eyes of their Venerable Foundress, religious. "I had rather the Society was ruined than that the vocation of one of my daughters should be exposed to danger," she said. Poverty? St. Ignatius had shown that all other virtues followed in its wake. She could wish few things better for them than poverty with its chosen companions, humility and joy.

Most surely God directed all things for their greater good. But while they were to be detached from their goods, she must also try to save the goods of the Society, since they were necessary for the education of children. As 1904 wore on, things worsened. They told her that M. Combes had said, "One effort more, and we shall have destroyed in less than two years the work of moral servitude of a century." She would not let her nuns say a bitter word against him, for all his rabid hatred of religion.

"He has taught us we must not cling to the things of this earth; he has given us a greater liberty of spirit by separation and detachment. He has shown us how many things are not really necessary."

On July 7th M. Combes struck again. By the law of that date, no teaching order, authorized or unauthorized, had permission to carry on: there was to be no recruitment of members, and all were to be suppressed within ten years. For each a liquidator was appointed to administer the goods of the congregation struck by the law and to operate its liquidation.

But on April 29th Mother Digby had put into safety the greatest treasure of her congregation. The incorrupt body of the humble Madeleine Sophie Barat had been taken from the vault at Conflans, and the leaden coffin placed in a new oak one. In the dark of the spring day the hearse had driven off to the station and the train had borne this daughter of France away to a new resting-place at Jette St. Pierre in the Belgium that was opening hospitable doors to other exiles. Sister Richardson, silent among the nuns left behind, watched the quiet tears flow down Mother Digby's cheeks.

Chapter Thirty

1904

THE Liquidator parted his hair and brushed it with care. It gave him a feeling of importance to be in charge of the affairs of the Society of the Sacred Heart. Besançon, Laval, Niort, Perpignan, Toulouse, Montfleury, Amiens, the cradle of the Society, Poitiers, the first noviceship, La Neuville, Charleville, Lille, Calais. Memory sent the list of closures from this year 1904 back for his consideration. A formidable list, satisfactorily dealt with . . . not by himself personally on the spot . . . but today's case was different. Paris, its importance warranted his presence . . . a touch of wax on his mustache . . . the police agent would have delivered the blue form; they would have grown familiar with its appearance after receiving so many now at the Mother House. His tie needed just slight adjustment. He would see the Mother General; they said she was old, in her seventieth year, a pity . . . he was not of those impervious to the plight of the vanquished . . . the *"Vae victis!"* did not rise easily to his lips. He buttoned his coat; the occasion demanded a certain solemnity. He selected a new pair of gray kid gloves, took his silver-topped stick. He would pay a *visite de convenance* today and settle the date for the inventory to be made.

The sunlight was pleasant this August afternoon with the shade of the trees for shelter. Passing along on the outside of the walls of the garden of the Sacred Heart, he felt a sense almost of proprietorship. There would be three buildings here to liquidate . . . the boarding school, 77 rue de Varenne, the retreat house and day school at Number 31 and the Mother House itself, number 33. A pleasant situation, all on the same property. He wondered what use they would be put to, when the religious had left. He wondered what the Mother General would do. They said she was English; no doubt she would find a quiet place in England in which to end her days. He would do his best to make the break easy for her.

He had his hand on the bell now. A Sister was showing him into a parlor. It seemed that she had not understood his importance . . . surely he should have been put in one that at least had curtains up and an easy chair to sit in. He sat upright on the old chair she had offered him, and waited.

A nun appeared. He rose, hat in hand.

"Have I the honor to address the Superior General?"

She smiled, almost amused, it would appear, by his mistake.

"No, I am her Assistant."

Assistant! That would then be Mother Borget. He remembered how a friend had told him that the order had gone round at the Post Office dealing with the watch on the correspondence of religious: "Read Borget." A formidable woman, holding the purse strings. What a pity it was not the Mother General! He spoke:

"I regret that I cannot see her in person: I came here to pay my respects . . . to make it clear that I do not come here as an adversary. You are aware that by the judgment of the tribunal I have been named liquidator of all the goods of your Congregation in France?

"I have adopted this delicate mission," he went on, wishing more than ever that it was Reverend Mother Digby he was approaching, "in order to fulfill it with every consideration. . . ."

Under her unwavering gaze, he heard himself explaining

his desire to safeguard their interests . . . to receive their little complaints or requests, to see that their alimentary pensions, permitted to them by the law, were properly paid . . . to perform the necessary action of obtaining the funds for these by liquidation . . . to make every allowance for them within the bounds of conscience . . . to permit them to carry away all their personal belongings, their books, sheets, beds, if they still had them . . . that the inventory would be purely a matter of form. . . .

It dawned on him suddenly that the room he was in had significance. He had heard rumors of denudations anticipating the action of the law. Perhaps the inventory would prove neither long nor complicated. He asked that a day might be fixed. He felt Mother Borget's eyes on him. It did not lie with her to answer. At last he would get a direct answer from the Mother General. He waited while a messenger was sent to her, laying one gray kid glove on the other. The interview had not worked out according to plan. The speech he had made had not fallen on the right ears. The parlor seemed somewhat close with the sun pouring through the unshaded windows.

The messenger had returned. He listened to the reply with pained surprise.

". . . As the taking of the inventory is an act the religious do not accept, but must undergo, it is not fitting that we should fix the day. We leave the choice to the gentleman who must perform it." There was nothing for it. In the silence that fell once the message was delivered, he found himself fixing August 8th. That would give them four days to understand his action the better. He picked up his walking-stick, his gray kid gloves, the door was opened before him. Mother Borget's eyes were still upon him. Was it a twinkle in them that he detected? At the threshold he turned.

"Must undergo!" he said sorrowfully. "What a word to use when I have come here expressly to signify my consideration and good-will."

The sparrows scuffling in the dust among the leaves that had already dropped from the trees looked offensively cheerful as he took his way home.

At the office the next day he was shown a letter received by the police after delivery of the notice of closure. He read with growing dismay. Was this the style of the Mother General?

"In my quality of Superior of this House of Paris, authorized by Decree of April 22nd, 1827, and as Superior General of the Society of the Sacred Heart of Jesus, I protest against all acts contrary to our rights. Being by our authorization under the guardianship of the Government, we have the right to claim the protection that every ward should receive from his guardian. That is only justice, and no one can deny it. And instead of this, you come to give me notice of closure in the name of the Government. My duty is to oppose it all the time. I ought to do so, and I do so formally. I will make appeal to the justice of men, and above all to the justice of God."

He shrugged his shoulders. It was not quite in good taste to bring in the Almighty in this matter. Thank God most of them who had to deal with the religious were impervious to that sentimental appeal. And as for the justice of men, they had the law on their side. There were all the enactments of the past years to support them.

The pearl-gray gloves were not quite so soft as he drew them on in the early morning of August 8th. He was joined by his notary, his secretary and his valuator. In silence the portress showed them into the large parlor. Their boots sounded noisy on the uncarpeted floor. He stood hesitant by the door, taking in the fact that in the middle of the bare room five nuns were seated facing them, while behind them he recognized M. Guyot-Sionnest, the solicitor, with his notary and clerk. He took refuge behind the table placed for him near the door, naming himself and his companions. As they sat down, the short nun in the midst rose, looking at him with blue eyes that seemed to read deep into his soul. Uncomfortably he glanced away, aware that this was the Mother

General whom he had thought to patronize in her discomfiture. She was reading from a paper she held in steady hands:

"In the name of the interests of which as Superior General I am the appointed guardian, and charged as I am specially with this house, I protest with all my might against the spoliation of which we are the victims. I affirm once again, and the State recognizes the fact as well as ourselves. . . ."

"Folly," he thought, "to have described her in the notification as 'proprietor' of the Paris House."

". . . our absolute right of property over all the goods of which you are about to take the inventory. Your laws may despoil us, but they cannot alter the fact that this house is ours: whoever the State may place here, they will always be in a home that belongs to us. Today we yield to force against which unarmed nuns are powerless; but we know that the hour of justice will strike, bringing with it the reparation due to what we suffer. For our rights are imprescriptible."

The quiet, vibrant voice ceased. She was handing the paper to M. Guyot-Sionnest. The door had opened and, dignified as a queen, she passed through. The liquidator was speechless with surprise. He caught the eyes of M. Guyot-Sionnest and his two friends on him; worse, his own companions were looking at him, waiting for his lead.

"Ah, the Superior General does not even deign to remain until the end," he muttered.

"The Very Reverend Mother Digby has nothing more to do here," said M. Guyot-Sionnest.

"The *procès-verbal* has not yet been signed," he retorted.

"It can be taken to her room," answered M. Guyot-Sionnest, taking steps to insert her protest.

By the chimney-piece the valuator was idly examining its mouldings. His task was yet to be done. It would be simplified if the nuns' legal advisers would lend their co-operation . . .

perhaps for a fee, a handsome fee? M. Guyot-Sionnest refused with a decisive negative. The notary gave the liquidator short shrift too. There was to be no help for him from that quarter. The valuator must get on with his job as best he might. A clock outside chimed. He hastily took out his watch.

"I regret that I, too, shall be unable to stay to the end of this meeting. I have to see my children off to the seaside."

It sounded lame. He was conscious of four pairs of eyes looking at him from the central table where the nuns had sat in silence. He bowed, and gathered up the pearl-gray gloves lying abandoned on the bare table before him. Somehow he got through the door and out into the Paris streets. He would never again set foot in the house while Reverend Mother Digby was there.

Left alone, the valuator turned to Reverend Mother Borget. "I suppose I may begin now?"

She began the rounds of the three houses with him, warning him that the nuns of the Community who were left had begun their retreat the night before and would be keeping absolute silence. He would find them engaged on their various household tasks, or in their own cells. It was uncanny, he thought, like walking round a kind of Sleeping Beauty's Palace, where he hadn't the clue to what was happening. His guide paused at a large door: "The chapel," she said.

He pushed open the door, then stood rooted on the threshold. Nothing but bare walls with the floor, swept and empty, between. He turned to Mother Borget.

"The stalls, the benches, statues, the altar . . . where are they?"

"Gone," she said briefly, remembering the last Benediction, when the children of the Boarding School knelt on the bare floor before they left for Brighton, and seeing again the still form of Mother Digby sitting upright in her stall while the stone-masons took down the altar, block by block.

He shrugged his shoulders.

"Useless to spend time here," he said. "Kindly lead on."

She took him along empty corridors, with never a sign of curtains or cupboards or furniture. She opened the doors of the kitchens. Vacant shelves met his gaze, and ovens with all the coldness of unused furnaces. In a far corner, a sister was busied about a few pots and pans, while a cauldron of soup steamed on a small range.

"You don't seem to have many utensils to cook with, Sister," he remarked, jotting down basins, saucepans, rolling-pins, and adding a table to his column of furniture.

"Quite enough, thank you—we have no children now," she answered, merely recording the fact.

They passed along by walls without pictures. Mother Borget saw in empty places this and that well-loved object, and sighed at the gap where the great statue of the Sacred Heart had stood before it was sent overseas to Brighton to welcome the exiled children there. The valuator, walking after her with echoing feet, sensed the presence of invisible things and people, almost as if the spirits of little children, laughing and bright-eyed, were following him round their deserted class-rooms and study-rooms and the places where they had played. It was a relief when his guide remarked, "These are the cells where the nuns who are left live."

He went in. He noted down a bed, a rickety chair, a plank across two packing-cases for a desk, a crucifix, a small valise.

"This nun is leaving today?" he enquired.

"No," said Mother Borget. "We are all packed ready for emergency. But we are not leaving today."

Each room was the same. Save for the crucifix of vows, no one had anything of value.

They came upon Mother Le Baïl on her knees before a large trunk. He turned hopefully to her. But she shook her head.

210

"No, this contains nothing but the letters and documents dealing with the beatification of our Holy Foundress," she said, and he left, noting down the usual minimum of furniture.

"The Reverend Mother General's room?" he asked. The door was indicated and he went in. Mother Digby was not there. He looked around, twiddling his pencil. No doubt this was where she had to assemble her councilors. That would account for the extra objects. He licked the pencil's point and wrote down: "A desk, four chairs, a stool." He hesitated a moment, summing up their value, then made up his mind. "Four francs," he noted, and moved on to the next room.

They came at last to a large room that had been transformed into a chapel. Here at least there were some things of value to be put down, but he shook his head at their fewness. "Our Lord shares our poverty," thought Mother Borget.

He left them at last. Only a good dinner with a bottle of wine was successful in removing the feeling of being haunted by ghosts of the past . . . or was it proximity to a present life that lay beyond his ken?

M. Guyot-Sionnest was delighted with his perusal of the *procès-verbal*.

"Reverend Mother, there are several flaws in this document. We can go on fighting the case."

"A delaying action," she said, "whose end is a foregone conclusion. But I shall stay here as long as I can and only move before force. We are maintaining our legal rights by living in these three houses, though it is only a handful of six or seven in each. The day school at Number 31 can go on for the time being, and the Poor School, and I can put into it, too, some boarders driven out of other houses, whose parents cannot send them outside the country. How can I thank you enough for what you are doing?" He smiled.

"By prayer, Reverend Mother. I say with the friend of mine who helps with the case of others of your houses, 'I have two account books: one for time, the other for eternity.' Your name is inscribed in the second."

Cardinal Richard came to see them. There was a wild search round for a suitable arm-chair for the old man. With real pleasure he sat on the only firm-legged, straight-backed chair they could produce. "I am happy to share your poverty," he said.

"I think," said Mother Digby, happy, too, in the thought, "that in all the Society there is no one poorer than my daughters of the Mother House."

"No one, except their Mother," said Mother de Pichon. She saw her Superior General as Cardinal Labouré had seen her . . . an admiral on his bridge. Like that admiral, she would be the last to leave the sinking ship.

The year moved to its close. Business over the Beatification took Mother Digby to Rome in the winter. In February 1905, Rome pronounced on the heroicity of the virtues of the Venerable Madeleine Sophie Barat. In March seven more houses were struck. Conflans was granted one more year of life. Litigation concerning the three houses of Paris lingered on. News came in July that Geraldine Digby had died. She would be sleeping in the quiet of Roehampton's cemetery, while her younger sister had still to bear the heat and burden of the fight. She visited the Belgian houses, and prepared to go again to Rome in winter.

On a golden September evening, Mother Justine de Kergos reached the Mother House, journeying all day from Marmoutier. Luscious dark grapes, rosy apples and velvet-skinned peaches filled the basket she carried and she laid it with some late roses before Mother Digby.

"Marmoutier's last gift," she said softly. Mother Digby looked at the ripe fruit and the beauty of the blooms.

"Sit down, Mother," she said, "and tell me all about it."

"I am glad that it is over now," said Mother de Kergos,

looking back in memory on the days that had passed since the cold January day when the policeman had delivered the blue notification at the old abbey. There had been the times of uncertainty, when the parents and friends had petitioned the councilors at Tours, and they in turn had passed on the petition to Orleans, and prefects, ministers, even ambassadors at Paris had intervened in their favor. Hope had been a will o' the wisp; it was easier when the last illusive light had gone. What a help Reverend Mother Digby's serene courage and confident abandonment to God's ways had been to them all through! Looking up into her kind eyes, blue still for all her seventy years, Mother de Kergos spoke of the end.

"The children were wonderful. They would not have prizes the last term; they would not cause us any further expense. You should have seen them praying in the chapel before they went from it for the last time."

The children . . . Mother Digby's thoughts ran back half a century. Those she had known were now the grandmothers of these, the same happy, buoyant young beings, with wells of seriousness and love of God beneath their exuberant love of the nuns and the dear places of their youth, heads bent over study books, chapel files, drowsy dormitories, laughter in class, prayers at the close of the day, well, that was all over now. . . .

"Their parents all came in person to take them away . . . they were in tears at the idea of others having charge of the education of their children. We went into retreat straight away."

The silence of the meadows under the watchful distant hills . . . the Loire running by . . . the cool of the chapel . . . the silence of Our Lord in His chosen tabernacle speaking deeper than words. . . . He had gone from it now. "Our obediences came on August 15th . . . you could not have chosen a better day, Reverend Mother. We took our heartbreak to Our Lady in her triumph and in a spirit of reparation and submission we renewed our vows in the chapel."

The vows to serve God in the Society of the Sacred Heart of His Son, by poverty, chastity, obedience and the education of youth . . . until death, that last act of faith where so many times He had heard her protestation of ultimate loyalty.

"The Municipal Council came in a body to express their regrets."

The Council with whom she had so happily co-operated in those hard days of want when the Prussians had overrun their loved countryside.

"The villagers came in their crowds to bid us good-bye, and there were crowds as the little groups of us left. Reverend Mother went on August 25th and left just eight of us as guardians. The big chapel was closed. We made a small one in one of the rooms on the Feast of the Holy Heart of Mary."

A little chapel. Our Lord humbly among His own . . . when the floods came from the Loire He had been there in the midst of them and had returned to His great chapel when the floods had run back.

"We had our rooms next to it, just the few of us in all the vast building."

Building for the future . . . bricks and mortar rising story by story . . . and the old monks sleeping while the newcomers carried on God's better work of raising a temple not built with hands. She had never taken satisfaction in the mere buildings. Their work was in the souls of those who had lived there.

"Mothers, aunts, Old Children, they all came to help us with our Benedictions and then turned to, to help us pack. . . . The liquidator arrived full of complaints before August was out. On September 2nd the Commissioner of Police came to see if we were still there and again on the 4th to know our names. The liquidator sold all our grapes."

Sunshine on the hillsides . . . laughing nuns in their blue aprons piling the vintage into tall wicker baskets . . . the sloping shadows as they came back . . . the clustering gray walls of the old abbey gathering them in like grapes ripe for the plucking.

"He watched all that went on . . . prowled about the grounds as though they belonged to him and went up to our men at work on the land and threw out his chest: 'We shall keep up this fine property . . . we must make it yield all it can!' 'We? Not on your life,' they answered him. 'We work only for the Sacred Heart and we're leaving with the Ladies.' "

Gauthier looking out over the fields . . . appraising the cattle . . . pulling up the beetroots as the flood waters seeped up . . . this was his spirit.

"We packed up and sent off all we could, but you know that they made an ejectment order for us and cited us to appear before the judge. We could only call in the Little Sisters of the Poor and let them take away anything of use to them and send a lot of things round to the orphanage at St. Radegond. Then yesterday we went to Mass for the last time . . . the Blessed Sacrament left the house, and we went into Tours for our interrogation."

The House empty and desolate . . . as when Madeleine Sophie Barat looked out on it across the Loire close on a century before.

"The judge had only three questions to ask us: Why we had remained at Marmoutier? Didn't we know the law and the notification given in January? And whom were we obeying in acting as we did? He did not get much satisfaction from us. We heard him mutter that he had rather deal with an assassin than with the nuns. We went back for our bags. The grottoes, with M. St. Martin, are in other hands now. That is all, Reverend Mother."

All? M. St. Martin would know how to look after his own.

Now there were but nine houses left in France. But there were many other houses being opened where before none had existed. In England, the students of the Training College had grown in number . . . the Cardinal of Westminster wanted them now in his diocese. The college in St. Charles' Square made it possible to have a hundred girls to train so that they could make better known the love of God.

1906 came and with it disasters straight from the hand of God, uncomplicated by the sins of men: San Francisco and Menlo Park damaged by earthquake, Portici wrecked by the eruption of Vesuvius, their houses in Chili, Valparaiso and Talca destroyed by fire.

On December 17th, the noise of shouting filled the whole road outside the Mother House. The aged Cardinal Richard was being turned out of his home. It was to have been done discreetly in the early morning, but the news got round. The nuns, watching from the windows, saw his carriage moving slowly through a dense mass of people, drawn by soldiers of rank, while the procession before and after sang the Creed and cried out, "We want God!" The old man looked up as he drew near the Mother House and raised his hand in blessing. It would be their turn next.

"They have stuck up a notice on our walls 'House to let'!" cried Mother Le Baïl a few days later.

"Have it removed," said Reverend Mother Digby imperturbably. The work of the Society went on.

But in July 1907, she read the signs aright. In the dusk of evening the workmen of the Mother House took their axes out to the garden and began to cut down the great cedar. As the strokes rang out, it seemed to her that a great link with the past was going. Never more would its massive trunk and widespreading branches be pointed out and wondering folk be told: Beneath its shade a saint gathered the little children for whom she had given her long life, and spoke to them of the Kingdom of Heaven, whose citizens they were. A crash that shook the ground. The cedar tree, Madeleine Sophie Barat and the Junior School belonged now to that realm of ideas beyond the touch of men's sacrilegious hands.

On August 7th came the blue form with the order "Evacuate immediately and without delay." On August 10th the last Mass said in the old Probation Room that had seen so many hundreds of young nuns preparing for their final vows. At one o'clock Mother Digby gathered the few remaining nuns around her for the recreation of rule. By five, only the Assistants General were left with her in the vestibule. Empty rooms lay all around them, with a desolate quietness unbroken by the least sound within. Outside, the rolling of wheels and the whinny of a horse told that the carriage was waiting for them. Mother Digby stood a moment in silent prayer, then turned and pulled down a large sheet of paper that had been pasted up opposite the main door. In large black letters a notice appeared for all who might enter to read.

"The Superior General of the Religious of the Sacred Heart of Jesus, driven out by force from the houses of which she is the lawful owner and despoiled of the property which belongs to the Congregation, protests with all her might against the sacrilegious violation of her rights. She reminds whoever takes possession of this property, or purchases it, that by that very act he comes under the sentence of major excommunication, which cuts him off from the body of the Church, and that absolution from this penalty can only be granted him by the Pope after restitution of the property usurped, and reparation of the harm done."

She closed the door behind her . . . the last nun of the Sacred Heart to leave the House that had for so long been the center of all hearts. Conflans lay ahead, a last stronghold for the Mother House on French soil. In the deserted buildings of the rue de Varenne, the flies were buzzing against the window panes hot in the August sun.

Chapter Thirty-one

1908—1909

ANTOINETTE BARBIER caught sight of her as the crowd began to break up before the station of the Bois de Boulogne. She threaded her way through to Françoise Duval.

"Fancy seeing you . . . up from Touraine? Let's go somewhere out of this crush, and talk."

The café by the sidewalk gave them a chair, and the opportunity of turning tired soles upwards.

"Not so young as we were," sighed 'Toinette, ordering two bocks. "Touched seventy, I have, and I'm not up to much work now, just a bit of charring from time to time. I reckon someone else can do the work when you've reached that age. Well, did you get a good place in the station?"

"Bit crowded," said Françoise, her eyes following the unaccustomed stream of motor-cars along the road. "But it was worth it. He's a lovely gentleman. Pity he'd to wait so long for his old mother to die off. I saw him once when he was Prince of Wales, on his way to Biarritz . . . they say now he's King Edward VII there'll be more of the Entente Cordiale between us. Keep the Prussian Kaiser in his place."

"Like as not," said 'Toinette, loosening a boot button. "He's plenty of pluck. Look at him last year coming through to Paris on May Day. They say they didn't want him to come, wanted him to have the Prefect of Police but he didn't mind;

218

he didn't seem a bit disturbed with all the cheering just now. That's his English way."

"Like Reverend Mother Digby," Françoise agreed. "Don't I remember her when the Prussians came to Marmoutier. . . . I was a kid then, but I've not forgotten. We've none of us forgotten her . . . you should have seen us all go along to the abbey ten years ago, when she'd been made Mother General and came to see the old place . . . she'd not forgotten us either . . . knew my name still . . . gave my brother's son his fare so's he could go to his daughter's clothing, had him up to Paris, too, before she sent the girl to America when they shut down Rennes. . . ."

'Toinette broke in, "That's just like her. Some years back now my daughter's man was down on his luck. I wasn't getting much myself . . . she'd a child. . . . Reverend Mother Digby spotted the two of them saying their prayers in the chapel. Here, she says, them two's not having enough nourishing food; here, she says, is an order for you. Hand it in to the dairy and you'll get the milk you need. You should see the little'un now, great strong girl. She'd be a nun if they was allowed. Shame, I calls it. What's happened down your way?"

Françoise sighed.

"They let the school buildings . . . the man that took over turned the big classroom into a low-down pub . . . and when pilgrims come along, not knowing what's happened, and want to see the grottoes and say their prayers to St. Martin, they're made to pay to go into them . . . like a common sort of show."

"You should see the Mother House here," said 'Toinette angrily. "It's a public scandal. When the nuns had gone, the liquidator sent a whole lot of us in to do some charring. Well, clean as a new pin it was, the way they left it. I downed my pail, and went and found the man. 'Look,' I says, 'it's robbing you to take your money for this . . . eat off the floor, you could,' I says. And then he goes and puts in a whole lot of workmen and shop girls and folk that don't hold to the Ten Commandments. The state the place is in! Dirt and mess . . . rooms where all them holy nuns used to live . . . the room where our Mother Barat died . . . no one cares a jot."

"Queer," commented Françoise, "and the Holy Father going to make a saint of her. There'll be a great to-do in Rome in May. Saints . . . well, they go about like other people, I reckon. Reverend Mother Digby used to make me think of them. She'd the peace of heaven in her face; I'd like to see her again before I go back to Tours."

"You'd find her changed, maybe," said 'Toinette. "She's been ill a lot. She don't move round so active now . . . takes someone's arm. I saw them helping her into a carriage the other day. Yes, she's got old, same as me. I says to her, 'Reverend Mother, the more I thinks about it, the more I see I'm just like you.' She looks at me with them blue eyes of hers and says, 'If so, how I pity you!' . . . sort of smiling and serious mixed."

'Toinette felt disconsolate, as if her world, the world she knew, was a wraith, and she left with no part in the new existence that was thrusting its blatant way forward. It had swallowed up the Mother House of the Sacred Heart, where she had worked and prayed for so long. Its hungry maw was waiting this one year and then Conflans would go . . . and with Conflans, Reverend Mother Digby. . . .

Old, tired and suffering, the Reverend Mother General had journeyed that March of 1908 to Jette St. Pierre. Rome had spoken, the miracles and holiness of the exiled Foundress had been recognized. Her Beatification was fixed. As the train brought her nearer to the frontier of Belgium, Mother Digby thought, "This is the seal of God placed on her work, on our Rule which led her to holiness. She has shown us the way. We must walk forward in it generously. The vine has been pruned by persecutions in so many countries and the life of the Society has grown rich and vigorous, but it is her spirit that we need. Thank God I find it in all kinds of places like leaven, among our Sisters, whose work brings them so close to the House of Nazareth and life with God, among those who are in the full tide of activity and are striving to imitate the public life of Our Lord, among those privileged ones whose only work is to suffer while the Sorrowful Mysteries of the Passion of Jesus Meek and Humble of Heart are engraved in their souls. Yes, souls like these are everywhere and we could be of their number; we don't need anything extraordinary, no exceptional natural gifts, no particular circumstances or means, just where we are is the place, the employment, the time, the conditions. Love, the gift of self, our fidelity, that is all."

The exhumation required by the Church took place on March 27th. She waited while the seals of the coffin were broken and then gazed once more on the loved face of Madeleine Sophie Barat, brown, like old ivory, but intact. Reverently she helped to remove the torn fragments of the habit and to clothe her anew. There was a fresh white cap for the venerable head. Gently she held that head between her hands and slipped the cap over it. A great prayer rose up in her heart for all her daughters, hers only because they were the saint's, that they should make a full and generous response to all that should be asked of them, that they should all be one, that the trial of persecution should strengthen that union in the measure of the bond of common suffering. She laid back the head that had bent forward in her hands; she must leave her now while the ecclesiastical representatives awaited fresh instructions from Rome.

They came by April 30th. What God had kept intact should not be touched for relics. The incorrupt body should be enshrined with all due solemnity beneath the altar of Our Lady of Seven Dolors. It lay in the open coffin for them to see a little longer. A new ring was to be placed on the finger of the right hand that had worn the pledge of total donation to Christ for the sixty-five years of working life. Mother Digby took the thin circlet and untwined the fingers clasped as in prayer about the rosary that had crumbled away, then gently passed it over the finger-tip and into position. . . . She bent forward and kissed it as so often she had done when that vital small hand had traced a little cross on her forehead and had extended itself in blessing over this least of her daughters. She would kneel now beside her and pray for the rest of her daughters, placing all the future of her Little Society in her hands, so that as her own body had remained whole and entire, so should she keep her religious family, ever united and through the ages free from corruption of slackening and growing cold of faith. Joy, happiness, gratitude, a fresh fervor in the service of Christ, love, glory, these would all fill their hearts to overflowing when on May 25th they all met in Rome for the Beatification . . . the silent form beside her had kept them all safe through the disintegration of persecution and banishment. . . .

She journeyed back again to Conflans, finding the way long and weary. The doctor saw her. He knew her character and said bluntly that there could be no question of a journey to Rome in her state of health. The Society was thunderstruck; her joy was to have been theirs. She smiled and set about making those arrangements which would hide the fact of her absence as much as was humanly possible. Pius X listened attentively while they told him of the disappointment; he had grown to know this woman who, like himself, had been loaded with high dignities they would have had none of. Like her, he smiled too.

"Yes, for her it is an immense privation, but her virtue is at the height of the sacrifice and worthy of the crown bestowed upon it."

222

To one of the nuns, kicking against the pricks, Mother Digby was explaining: "To suffer is an honor. It shows we are no longer privates but have risen in the army of the King. War is declared. The enemies of Jesus Christ are in battle array and we belong to the great opposing army. Never lower the standard."

Hers was flying high that happy week in May when Madeleine Sophie Barat was declared Blessed. With the few left in Conflans, she was more than a mother. They felt that heaven was very close and that she moved among the verities of life. Mother Du Chélas recollected the day in Poitiers when she had visited the first noviceship of the Society just after her election, and had spent so long a time in the chapel dear to Blessed Madeleine Sophie that they had become anxious. She had been unaware of her presence when Mother Du Chélas went into the chapel. Back in her room, at a late hour, she had seemed still absorbed in eternity.

"Did you see Our Blessed Mother Barat?" Mother Du Chélas asked, greatly daring.

"One does not speak of this sort of thing," Mother Digby had answered, and Mother Du Chélas had known that she could not question further.

"Don't tire yourself too much," one of those left behind ventured to suggest. "You're giving us so much and doing so many things for us." Mother Digby smiled happily.

"Shouldn't you and I be happy to give our life to God? Let us give it Him drop by drop in each little duty."

"But, Reverend Mother, we've been at you all day long with one thing and another; there's someone waiting outside your room now . . . and I'm sure she hasn't anything important to say to you."

Again the happy smile came.

"A poor superior is hounded all day long and on all sides, but the last daughter who comes with some tiny insignificant matter has the right to be received as lovingly and as helpfully as the first!" Yes. Of course. That was the way Blessed Madeleine Sophie Barat had acted. They were seeing now the living example of her lesson well learned.

The golden days of 1908 faded into the grayness of the last few months of grace. On the Feast of the Sacred Heart, in June 1909, two hundred Children of Mary came to say good-bye. This would be their last meeting on French soil in a Convent of the Sacred Heart. On July 1st, the boarding school children had their prize day: the last boarding school left in France. Mother Digby was still busy with new foundations.

"Isn't it better to found than to founder?" she had asked with a laugh. Mother Le Baïl brought her a post growing daily heavier. With all her accustomed clearness of grasp and accuracy of memory, she dealt with it. When the afternoon's business was over, she rose quickly and made for the chapel.

"It's only ten to four," Mother Le Baïl said one day. "You will be a long time in the chapel."

"Long!"

Mother Le Baïl knew the word was not addressed to her. That radiant look on her face anticipated the moments when she would be before the tabernacle . . . plunged into another world where for the Loved One sorrow and persecution were at an end. He was there, she had said, in the depths of the sanctuary, and He would draw our hearts and desires to Himself alone. Now she was sinking deeper and deeper into the Mystery of the Eucharist, living those two words which summed it all up: He was subject: He was silent.

The corridors of Conflans were silent now. The children had gone. It was as quiet as when Blessed Madeleine Sophie went there to greet her novices, but desolation had fallen on it. On July 28th, Mother Digby wrote to her niece:

"I write surrounded by every sort of luggage, for we leave this on Friday, when we are turned out of this house where I made my novitiate and my vows fifty-two years ago, in the joy of my heart. Who would have thought it would come to this. We have now twenty-two nuns on the sea and how bravely they started for Japan, Brazil, New Zealand, Australia, Buenos Aires, the United States and so on. Pray for them, and for your poor old Aunty Mabel, who loves you dearly."

Crowds of friends, poor people and rich, invaded the house at the end. They knelt on the floor of the chapel and with outstretched arms sang the Parce Domine, the Creed, and received the last Benediction. On July 30th the last Mass was said in this last sanctuary of the Society of France. In the Paris diocese it was the Feast of St. Ignatius. "All those who would live holily in Jesus Christ will be persecuted," came its message. The few nuns who were left climbed into the waiting carriages. Mother Digby took her place. Little groups of silent people watched them as they drove out by the gate, mothers holding up their children to get a last blessing from them.

Beyond the fields, the Seine flowed low in the summer drought.

Chapter Thirty-two

1909—1911

A T Ixelles the Mother House was coming to life again. The autumn gales were tearing the leaves from the trees and sending them swirling down the Brussels streets, but the last packing-case had been opened and files and ledgers were in position and Mother Borget was carrying on business in more stable surroundings than trunks and boxes, and Mother Le Baïl writing on a more secure surface than a plank. The thirty-two happy probanists, those young nuns who in the five years since noviceship and first vows had learned to live the life of prayer and apostolic work, had been called from their different countries to begin again the six-monthly gatherings at the center of the Society before making their final vows. They brought the promise of summer with them, and Mother Digby, sitting in their midst for recreation, would look long at their faces turned towards her, so full of life and joy, and wonder what the future held for them. She spoke to them of their foundress, of the holy nuns she had known, of the Society she loved so dearly, of the distant works and those near at hand, of the power of prayer and the honor of suffering. It was as though she was reading into the very hearts of those listening to her, as though she would give all she had to make them generous in the service of their Lord to carry on the work that she had so soon to hand over to others more worthy than herself. The children of the boarding school had to go elsewhere, but the Poor School and the evening classes and meetings of congregations remained. It was good to have this opportunity of working for the little ones so dear to the Heart of Christ, and to be able to carry on the work of teaching at the Mother House. Teaching was not an addition but belonged to the very essence of their Constitutions. She knew that of all these young religious rejoicing in the months of contemplative life before they were scattered again to the uttermost parts of the earth, most of them would reach their sanctity through the humdrum and ever-changing work of the class-room. Yes, when death came to them, their great regret would be, like hers, not to have done all they could for God. And how glad they would be, like her, of this life's little pin-pricks.

Sister Richardson was not so sure about the pin-pricks. Night after night she knew the Mother General had been sleepless with pain. Yet morning after morning she would be up at the hour of rule and in the chapel. She did not dare to expostulate too much, but she said her say. Mother Digby smiled at her.

"Now, Sister, when you come to call me in the morning, you are not to say 'Oh, Reverend Mother, you really ought not to get up for Mass after such a bad night,' or anything of that sort; but just this, 'The beast must get up!' "

Mother Le Baïl wondered at her endurance.

"It looks as if you really loved suffering."

"Yes, I do, indeed," she said, thinking of the evil that man wrought against his Maker, and the need to repair in company with His Son's sufferings.

"And how do you manage to reach that love?"

"We have to practice much, and make efforts, and ask insistently for grace." She was looking back at the long years of her life. How cowardly she had been!

"And what pains have you taken to reach it?"

"Well, once, for instance, I wrote the name of Jesus on a little paper. I begged of Him the strength to suffer until such an hour, then I began again."

"I think I should not have the courage."

"You must cry out for it in prayer. You must beg for it. Your old Mother is like you: she needs a steam engine behind to push her on."

Cardinal Mercier of Malines came to the Convent. It heartened him to know so valiant a fighter in the cause of right. To have her in his diocese was an inspiration. Perhaps he would need something of her fearlessness in the years to come. Forty-six houses had been shut by the enemies of God. She had opened forty-six more in other far-flung lands where

God Incarnate tabernacled and radiated the love that would conquer the world. The victory was more than won.

But to her daughters it was the overflowing of her kindness that seemed so inexhaustible. She spoke to them of a gift of self to God so complete that each one might be treated as the 'thing' of God. She had given herself to them, too, so completely that they might treat her in like manner. Love went down to the hard depths of speaking candidly of faults and failings, but her love was always clear. Now, as the months ran by, compassion and motherly tenderness met each who came to her.

An English probanist went to her, heart-heavy.

"Life is passing so quickly . . . you are growing old . . . I shall never see you again when I go. . . ."

Mother Digby looked down at her, at the sensitive heart that could not find words for all its pain. Youth, youth . . . with the bruises of life still to come. . . . She bent over her.

"Feel, you must, dear child. You would not be human if you did not. But go to the chapel. There you will find help and strength."

Help and strength came, too, from the wells of her own calm serenity. She smiled, looking out into the future. "When I die, you will see how I shall help you . . . leave the future to God . . . but now don't be long before you come to talk to me again."

On December 2nd Essex died. She wrote as soon as she heard to her nieces, to cheer them with eternal thoughts of the unfailing love of Christ for his soul. How good to hear that all his thoughts at the end were for others and never for himself! They had all gone before her now into the light of life . . . Gertrude, Kenelm, her father, Eva, her mother, Geraldine . . . and last, Essex. There was no one left to remember with her the sharp joys and sorrows of childhood, in all their bright colors. The things of those days were very

near in memory, oases of simplicity in the crowded years of
labor and responsibility: little things of no importance, evok-
ing a world where love felt deeply for those who shared the
life of home . . . the smell of strawberries, hot in the sun,
the fragile earthiness of mushrooms speaking of the green-
sward of English downlands under the fresh sky of early morning, the smooth glide of carriage wheels on the leisurely way
to Bath, the plunging hoofs of hunters, box hedges and the
laughter of a little boy, a chair where her mother had sat
upright while she crept to the door to wonder at her beauty,
the roughness of her father's coat as he caught her to him . . .
good things, living now only in her mind, reflections of the
better things laid up in heaven, beauty of earth, transient and
inapprehensible, so full yet so faint in the light of the beauty
of Christ. Once He had been glimpsed, all earth was but a
waiting place. The words she had found in an old prayer book
were daily more real to her. . . .

> For ah! the Master is so fair,
> His smile so sweet to banished men,
> That they who meet it unaware
> Can never rest on earth again.
>
> And they who see Him rise afar
> At God's right hand to welcome them
> Forgetful stand of home and land,
> Desiring fair Jerusalem.

All the fairness of earth. She had seen it in intense vitality
that day ten years ago, when the sun had sunk in glory between two ranges of mountains in California, as she had come
from the calm peace of Benediction and the light of the spirit
had flowed into the light of creation and she had wanted to
hold it for ever, and the realization had come that in a little
while her place would know her no more. It had moved her
to tears to see it so lovely and to think that in a few years

she would be gone. Foolish, they were all moving forward through the journey of life to something far beyond all this. She was glad that she had seen all her dear ones go before her. . . .

> Praise God! The Master is so sweet;
> Praise God! The country is so fair.
> We would not hold them from His feet,
> We would but haste to meet them there.

The new year came, and with it death drew near. All through January the warnings were clear . . . pain and suffering and sleeplessness lowered her powers of resistance and on the first Friday of February she was taken very ill. The doctors gave no hope. Mother Borget went to her.

"Reverend Mother, do you want anything?" She smiled.

"Yes, I wish to become holy."

"Well, God offers you the means. To the sick He sends His priest with the Holy Oils."

The smile was on her lips again.

"I understand. Whenever you like."

She was filled with great happiness after Extreme Unction, silent for the most part. But on the following day she said, "God is good, immensely good. I long for heaven . . . but I am ready to live on."

Her daughters watched with growing sorrow her increasing weakness. On February 10 she became unconscious. The assistance of this world was fruitless: heaven alone might help. Mother Borget asked the nuns to make a novena through the intercession of the Venerable Mother Duchesne. Mother Digby had done so much for the introduction of her cause: surely she would help them. The doctors shook their heads. There could be no hope.

"Father," said Dr. Hilson's little daughter to him one day during the novena, "I dreamed that Our Mother General was cured . . . not by you. By God, the best doctor of all."

230

He looked at her incredulously. The novena had ended and no improvement had come. The nuns began again. On February 28th she seemed a little better. On the first Friday of March she was up again in her chair, a little sad at returning to "this lower world of ours," but ready to "suffer and to help gain souls for our dear Lord," as she said.

There was work to do still, since He needed her. The time had come round for the general Congregation of the Society to meet for the sixteenth time since its foundation. There was so much to be thankful for, God's visible protection of them in the difficult years just gone through, so much to prepare for a future of changed needs and new fields of apostolate requiring adaptations while the basis of all remained unchanged, so great a call to renewal of fervor and an ever-deepening charity and humility . . . humility and charity . . . when these two virtues were found together in a soul, then the true spirit of the Society was found . . . something of the gentle kingliness of Jesus Christ passed into that soul . . . a royal soul . . . a perfect religious life. She wrote to thank them for their prayers on her behalf, which had made it possible for her to take part once more in the work so dear to them all. "I cannot pretend not to regret having been so near the goal and yet having come back. I count on your prayers to sustain me in whatever work God will allow me to do for His glory and for the Society to which I owe my life and to which I shall devote what remains to me of it. . . ."

Time was passing, was flying. The great day of meeting Christ was drawing nearer, Christ whom alone she wished to love and serve. How short time was . . . and how clearly now she could see what waste was anything that was not done for God. She carried through the labors of the Congregation, spreading happiness among all the Mothers Vicar who came to it from all parts of the world. At its close there was a day more of heaven than of earth when she went with them and the Assistants General to Jette and knelt with them all around the shrine of Blessed Madeleine Sophie Barat. The past and present ran into one: the future completed the perfect cycle. One heart and one mind . . . Lord, keep this will of our hearts.

She went ahead of them back to Ixelles and was there waiting for them at the door as they returned in the mellow splendors of a late summer day, a great-hearted mother welcoming her daughters. That was how they would remember her in the months to come.

The winter came. The probanists grew used again to seeing her on the prie-dieu in the antechapel at seven in the evening, in full view of the altar, absorbed in the Presence there. In the morning they watched for her to come from Holy Communion to her room, so that they could see her lowered eyes, her head bent forward, and that air of being elsewhere than on dull earth. They paused unseen to see her wait long moments at her open door to say her good night to her Lord, through the open doors of the chapel. She spoke to them in confidence. The writings of Sister Thérèse of the Child Jesus came into her hands and she lingered over her message that it was not so much austerities that God asked for as humility and love . . . humility through love.

"Let your soul open out in the love of God," she said, "and your confidence will grow."

Spring broke through the bleakness of winter with birdsong and opening flowers. The Easter Candle heralded the Resurrection. The Paschaltide drew to a close. They celebrated her feast joyfully on the Patronage of St. Joseph. But she was not deceived.

"You are still young," she said to a visitor, "but I am seventy-six. I must prepare for death each day."

"Look," she said, handing the letter she had just written to Mother Le Baïl, "you see, I am not mistress of my handwriting. I am beginning to be as I was in February of last year."

But she would work on to the end.

On Monday, May 15th, she had a bad headache. At midday she went to the recreation of the Community, but, finding she was too early, put down her spectacles on her table, together with some photographs, and went away. The nuns saw them, and when she came back, were loud in their expressions of regret that they had not been there to meet her. She laughed and took the blame to herself. "I was not punctual," she told them. "True punctuality means coming at the right time, neither before nor after." She passed round the photographs and they saw how the new chapel of Granada had been helped by the gift of the stalls from the Ixelles chapel, which in turn had received those of the Paris Mother House. There was always good possible from the disasters men made.

Mother de Pichon kept them laughing with her stories. "I had a dream when I was superior at Montpellier," she narrated. "I saw the great statue of the Sacred Heart there suddenly come to life and descend from the pedestal and move towards me. I was ravished out of myself, and cried out, 'O dear Lord, let me go and look for my community too. . . .'"

"If it had been me," said Mother Digby, "I think I should have forgotten everything, even my daughters."

The recreation over, the work of the day went on. Seven o'clock drew near. Mother Digby finished her work, opened her door, and went forward to the prie-dieu. He was waiting for her there in the tabernacle, as He had waited for her so many long years ago, in the tabernacle at Montpellier. She knelt there, gazing at Him.

The clock struck the quarter. The sacristan at work by the High Altar heard the noise of a sudden fall. A young nun at her prayers rose with her and hurried down the chapel. Mother Digby lay on the ground. . . . She smiled at them. "I felt giddy. . . . I tried to sit down and missed my chair . . .

don't touch me." The Assistants General came to her. Sister Richardson was called in haste and her practiced eye took in the situation. The stroke had paralysed her right side completely. They carried her to her room, summoned the doctor, and on his insistence called the priest. She was very silent while he gave her the Last Sacraments.

"You are in God's hands?" he asked her.

"I hope so," she answered humbly.

"And you want everything that He wants?"

The answer came quickly: "Yes! Everything . . . everything."

With death in her heart Sister Richardson watched by her that night. Last year she had spoken to her, sorry that she was giving so much trouble. This year she lay with her eyes closed as though nothing on earth could touch her serenity. The night was full of pain and the morning found her weaker. As the day wore on, hope died away. Pius X sent a telegram with his blessing. It was placed before her, but she did not open her eyes.

One of the Mothers beside her whispered, "Your eyes are always shut. . . ."

"Always turned towards Jesus," she murmured.

"Would not this be more comfortable?" asked one of the Mothers, seeking to move a pillow, as she watched the tired hand pressed against the aching forehead.

"We must not seek what is more comfortable," came the quick rejoinder.

"What must we seek for, then?"

"For what pleases Him Most."

Silence fell again. Mother Borget came in. Sister Richardson said, "Here is Reverend Mother Borget."

"She is welcome . . . you don't know what care they are taking of me."

The Assistant General said slowly, "You are near the Blessed Sacrament."

Her eyes did not open, but a half-smile came upon her lips. "That consoles me." She did not ask for anything. From time to time, more to ease their own hearts, they tried to do something for her, and she met their attempts with a grateful "You are too good." Once she expostulated, "The beast is always trying to find comfort."

"There cannot be much comfort when you are so ill," sighed Mother de Pichon.

"Oh, yes," she answered. "There is the seeking for ease . . . that we must lessen."

The moments passed relentlessly. She lay still and calm. Someone lifted her coverlet to arrange it, saying as she did so, "This is heavy." Mother Digby's thoughts were on the office she had borne for sixteen years, and was still bearing. "Yes," she said, "it is a burden, but Jesus bears it with us." When she laid it down, it must rest on someone else's shoulders. That true thought would help to lighten it. Yes, Jesus bears it with us.

The evening fell. Sister Richardson was there, the faithful link with England and all the love that lay in Roehampton. In her own tongue she heard the prayer "Jesus, Mary, Joseph, I give you my heart and my soul." The second invocation began, but a great sob choked the utterance.

"Assist me in my last agony," whispered Mother Digby. Sister Richardson regained command of her voice and slowly repeated the *Memorare* and the *Anima Christi*. Then she asked, "What prayer do you like best?"

"The *Suscipe*," answered Mother Digby. There was silence. Then quietly she spoke the last words of the prayer, "Give me only Thy love and Thy grace . . . this is enough for me."

Wednesday came and went. Only, from time to time, she said, "How good our Master is!"

On Thursday, Mother Borget, seeing some slight rallying of powers, asked her, "Would you like to receive Our Lord?"

"Oh, yes!"

He came to her. Those who watched noticed she seemed to enter more deeply than ever into a world beyond their ken. Sister Richardson knew that this would be the last time she would meet Him veiled in signs.

"What message do you give your daughters?" asked Mother Borget.

"Tell them that I love them with all my heart."

"And in return?"

"That they should belong wholly to Jesus."

"And what message for the Society?"

"The same thing. . . ."

"That they should be united?"

"They are . . . but in a union growing ever more and more."

The day of suffering dragged on into the night.

"What shall we say to the probanists as your message?" she was asked.

"Many, many things . . . above all that they should love Our Lord with all their hearts."

"Love is everything?"

"Yes . . . everything."

"And what shall we ask for you?"

"That I should love Our Lord with all my heart."

Her voice sank into silence. Pain took her into its cleansing hands, and she yielded willingly. Those round about her could do little. Mother de Pichon sighed. Mother Digby heard her.

"What do you want, my child?"

"That you should be better, Reverend Mother."

"You could not want that."

"But if God wanted it?"

His will had always been hers . . . but again a smile played round the dying lips.

"There are things He likes better."

"What does He like better?"

"That we should suffer."

There was a pause. Then she said, leaning on the words as though her whole soul meant each syllable, "His Will is always adorable."

It was fitting that Friday should be a day of pain. She met pain with prayer. One murmured invocation followed another. In an interval of respite, she said aloud, in English, "Our Father, Who art in Heaven . . ." and kneeling beside her in the gathering dusk, Sister Richardson struggled to join in that Amen.

If only she could see once more the eyes of her beloved Mother fixed on her, those kind blue eyes that had read her joys and sorrows and the very depths of her soul, those eyes from which her Mother's soul had looked forth with all her love for an unworthy daughter. Even as the mute prayer was made, Mother Digby's eyes opened and she looked full into those of her faithful friend.

Sister Richardson whispered, "Reverend Mother, you want to go to heaven?"

"Yes, very much."

"Our Lord will receive you with great love."

"Yes, I hope so."

"Will you give me a little message for the Sisters?"

There was a pause, as though she was seeking for the very best legacy for them, putting her love for them into its ultimate form. Then she said, "They must be humble and devoted . . . everything is in that."

There was no other sound during the long night than her labored breathing. From time to time she made the sign of the cross. On Saturday she had so far lost ground that the priest gave her the Last Blessing. The nuns recited the prayers for the dying and she answered them in a faint voice. She held her rosary and her fingers moved from bead to bead. A stream of prayer flowed about her and the peace of God was in the little room. Mother Borget, beside her, asked towards the evening, "Do you bless all your daughters?"

"Yes." There was no doubting her assent.

"And all your children?"

"Yes."

"And our works?"

"Yes."

The tired right hand was lifted in a last blessing, following the beams of the Cross north, south, east and west, encompassing all she had mothered for so long. Mother Borget held the crucifix of her vows, made fifty-two years before, in front of her, and named the Sacred Wounds of Hands and Feet and Side. As though she was very close to that wide opening, she whispered, "Yes, the Sacred Side. . . ."

Darkness had crept up and the shaded lamp was lighted. Death was slow in coming. Sister Richardson prayed on and watched, while memories came quietly to her wondering mind. Did Reverend Mother Digby see again the Sacred Host uplifted in the Church at Montpellier . . . the chapel at Conflans and the white-veiled novices . . . the loving smile of the ageing Mother Foundress . . . the walls of Marmoutier and the daughters and children who were the first to call her Mother. . . . Were her thoughts, like her own, moving round the rooms and gray chapel and long corridors and busy kitchens and green lawns under the shady trees, with the rhododendrons out in rich bloom at Roehampton . . . with laughing Mother Kerr and old Sister Johanna and loving Reverend Mother Stuart and Mother Leslie and many another living or dead whose lives had been the keener for her presence . . . or was it the Mother House at Paris where she lingered, or the houses up and down Europe or in the length and breadth of America, where she had passed with the fire of the Sacred Heart . . . half a century of memories . . . filled to the brim with good things she had done: a robin taking crumbs from her hand, a soul shown the depths of God's love, a mother's smile for her child in the little insignificant things of daily life. In the silence, past and present seemed very close, as though God was holding all in the palm of His hand, no bigger than a little hazel nut, under His gaze.

Suddenly in the hush of the room, after a long silence, Mabel Digby spoke.

"Alleluia!"

There was nothing now but waiting until the glory should be revealed. Midnight passed into the first day of the week. Dawn broke early in the calm sky of May. The sun rose warm on the fresh green leaves of the trees, and birds sang with care-free joyousness. The clock chimed half-past ten. The long agony was drawing to an end. A few deep sighs . . . one last gentle breathing forth.

Behold, I come quickly, and my reward is with Me. Amen.

Come, Lord Jesus!

Alleluia!

Epilogue

ASCENSION DAY, May 25th, 1911, was bright with sunlight and bird-song. There had been thick fog over the Channel as they brought Mabel Digby back to England, but at Roehampton the early morning was still with the promise of noontide warmth. They carried the coffin into the side chapel where through the grille the radiant pink flowers on the High Altar spoke of the joy of heaven. Flowers spilling over the catafalque joined their praise before the Blessed Sacrament exposed. In that glory and glow she lay till sunset.

When the Requiem Mass of the next day was over, there were flowers scattering their pink and white petals from the apple trees and homely May bushes as the coffin was borne down the garden to the little cemetery. The souls she had loved were there following her . . . the nuns, the novices, the children of the boarding school, the little ones of the elementary school, and the students singing the *"In Paradisum."* The sun, breaking from behind a cloud, made the white lilies around the grave shine transparently and blackbirds and thrushes sang full-throatedly and a white butterfly fluttered unperturbed across the blossoms. Mabel Digby had come home.

But, in the fall of the year, her body was moved back to the place that had drawn her thoughts so often in life. In the Chapel of the Sacred Heart, to the left of the High Altar, near the mortal remains of the Roman martyr Sabbatia and the great French Jesuit, Father Joseph Varin, she was laid as though looking through to the tabernacle. A few years later she was joined by Janet Erskine Stuart, who had shouldered the burden she had laid down.

When the fire of war destroyed the house she had known and loved and labored for, and the chapel that had been its center, the flames stopped by the grille. In the untouched sanctuary of the Chapel of the Sacred Heart, Christ took up His abode and Mabel Digby lies very close now to the Lord who had given her so much in the Blessed Sacrament.

War's destroying action brought back also to their first home the successors of those students for whom in 1874 Mabel Digby had suffered and prayed. To them and to those who work with and for them in the task whose end is eternity, her message of an earlier day rings true: "Tell them to be souls of prayer."